The 60-Day Food and Fitness Program

& Journal

Brad Peterson

Fat Gram and Calorie Counter
Including Fast Foods

Plus...
Low-fat, low-calorie recipes,
exercise tips, and more!

> The approach taken in this book is considered by a majority of health care professionals to be the most effective program available for safe, long-term weight management.

1st Place MIPA Award Winner
Diet/Health/Fitness

Acknowledgments

Dr. Daniel Carey, Exercise Physiologist
Karen S. Husu, Registered Dietitian, Nutrition Consultant
Susan White, Registered Dietitian, Nutrition Consultant
Pat Morris, Editor
Tracy Ryman, Desktop Design Studio

Cover design by Deborah Pierce

Published in Minneapolis, Minnesota by

The Forever Fit Group, Ltd.
4145 Parklawn Ave. Suite 338
Edina, MN 55435
Phone: (952) 835-9998

ISBN 0-9728846-0-2

This book is not intended to provide medical advice or take the place of your doctor's advice. It is always best to consult your physician before beginning any diet or exercise program. Though *The 60-Day Food and Fitness Program* is as accurate as its author, publishers and medical consultants can make it, they disclaim any and all responsibility and liability for any possible consequences from its use.

About The Author

Brad Peterson, a noted spokesman, author and television personality, has enlightened and entertained audiences across the country. He is the author of three previous books and has operated fitness centers from Minneapolis, Minnesota, to Marina del Ray, California. Brad recently completed filming a television program on preventive health care with Mickey Rooney, Tom Hallick and Super Bowl quarterback, Jim Plunkett. He has been chosen to judge several beauty and talent pageants including the *2003 Mrs. Minnesota International Pageant.* Brad has also appeared in many principal roles in television programs, including L.A. Law, and in feature films such as The Mighty Ducks.

Look and feel 20 years younger when you read Brad's exciting and informative new book, *Forever Young,* coming soon. Also, watch for the Kid's Fitness Program later this year.

Contributing Authors

Karen S. Husu, a registered and licensed dietitian for 15 years, has developed nutritional programs for hospitals, fitness centers and corporations, including 3M and General Mills. She has written articles for various print media on weight management, cardiac health, diabetes, sports nutrition and eating disorders. She has also been a featured guest on numerous radio programs.

Dr. Daniel Carey is a professor in the Health and Human Performance Department of the University of St. Thomas. He is chair of the Healthy U Program, which was designed to promote healthy lifestyles. He conducts research on body composition, metabolism, fitness assessment and athletic performance. For the past 10 years, Dan has developed cardiac rehab programs for various hospitals and has tested Olympic athletes.

My sincere thanks to two of the most highly respected health and fitness experts in the country for their collaborative efforts in bringing this project to fruition.

Brad

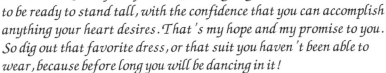

A Letter from the Author

Be ready when life calls!! Ready to look in the mirror and be proud of what you see. Ready to go out and live life to its fullest! No more missing out because you feel too heavy, too tired, or lack in self-confidence. You're going to be ready to stand tall, with the confidence that you can accomplish anything your heart desires. That's my hope and my promise to you. So dig out that favorite dress, or that suit you haven't been able to wear, because before long you will be dancing in it!

There are overweight people who will tell you fat is beautiful and that they like the way they look. Bologna! Who wouldn't want to look better, feel better and live longer if they could? So, let's get real.

I want to say upfront that we will not make any outrageous claims or unrealistic promises. You will see as you work through the journal that we've taken a positive, commonsense approach that will teach you to take off the weight and change your life for the better.

What's that old saying? Give a man a fish and you've fed him for the day; teach a man to fish and you've fed him for the rest of his life. We're going to help you learn for yourself how to eat right. Then you will be able to create a realistic program that will fit your particular lifestyle. We're all different; a program that works for someone else may not work for you. When you're involved in creating your own strategy, it will be easier to lose weight and keep it off.

Weight loss isn't rocket science. Thousands of companies are making billions of dollars with their quick-fix programs, diet pills and supposed innovative exercise equipment – and they're your dollars. In reality, it's as simple as calories in (better food choices and portion control) and calories out (exercise).

Now that I've said that in theory weight loss isn't complicated, I must also say that actually losing weight isn't easy. That's why more than 95% of those who lose weight gain all of that weight back plus more. It will take the understanding you'll gain by using this book coupled with focused determination to succeed.

This book gives you the most accurate, up-to-date information available and allows you to monitor your progress. As you start to see results, you'll become more and more confident that you truly can lose weight. Keep in mind, though, that nobody's perfect. Don't beat yourself up if you have a bad day – just start again tomorrow. Occasionally there will be days when you will let yourself indulge, but you will pick those days wisely. As time goes by you'll see how wonderful it feels to get control over something you thought you couldn't control.

All the information and encouragement you'll need is in this book. If you're ever going to lose weight and keep if off, this commonsense approach and journaling is the way. But ultimately it's going to be up to you. You have to be mentally ready in order to get fit and, more importantly, stay fit. Once it happens in your mind, your body will follow. Henry Ford once said, "Whether you think you can or think you can't – you're right." So, which will it be?

From now on when life calls, you'll be ready!

Good Luck – you can do it!

Brad Peterson

Table of Contents

Introduction

This book is unique because it not only gives the information you need, but it offers the day-to-day hands-on monitoring it takes to lose weight and keep it off for a lifetime.

The first thing we discuss is how important it is for you to get yourself in the right mindset. You will visualize what a leaner, healthier you will look and feel like. Then you'll work on modifying your behavior to change the way you look at food. You'll discover that food can be your friend, not your enemy. You will identify those influences that cause you to eat more. As you become alert to those factors, you'll learn how to substitute new behaviors. You will gain a great deal of personal insight about yourself which you can then use to improve your overall health and appearance. You will set realistic (achievable) goals for your age and height. You'll determine how much you need to lose and break that down into small weekly goals. You will record your measurements at the beginning, the middle, and at the end of the journal.

We repeatedly say "you'll learn to..." Why? Because that's what this hands-on journaling approach is all about – you learning (not just reading about but really learning) and understanding how to put this information into day-to-day practice.

Next, you'll learn how to establish calorie and fat gram limits. We'll elaborate on portion control and show you how to determine a serving size. The nutritional food value sections will allow you to see precisely how many calories you're consuming. As you develop a tailor-made program that works for you, you will make healthier choices. You'll find great low-calorie recipes, hints for reducing fat in your cooking and lighthearted quotes to encourage you as you continue to lose weight.

You will learn why it's important to incorporate both strength training and cardiovascular exercise into your weekly routine. We've included exercise charts to monitor your activities.

Each day is a record of what you've eaten, how much you've exercised and the calories you've burned. You will record the amount of water you are drinking each day, because water is a key ingredient to weight loss. There is also a place for you to record your emotions each day, so you can see how you handled certain situations that may have triggered the desire to eat. Correlations between your emotions and eating habits will become obvious as you review your journal and you will be able to determine where adjustments to your program are needed. Journaling will influence you to make better choices in the future. As you see the progress you have made, you will feel motivated to continue on your road to fitness.

Note: Although this book is titled *The 60-Day Food and Fitness Program*, it's really a step-by-step guide about how to manage your nutrition and exercise on an on-going basis. Don't let journaling overwhelm you. It only takes a few minutes each day and it gets easier as you become familiar with the book.

On The Road

To Fitness

Charting Your Way

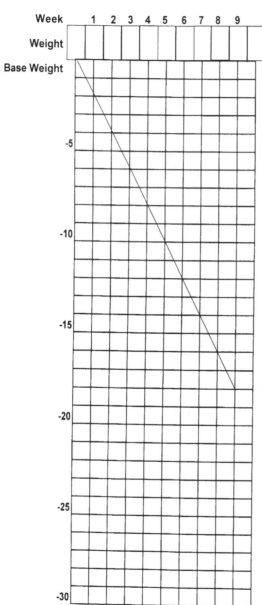

Graphing your weight loss is an effective visual aide used to view the progress of your weight reduction. Start your beginning or base weight as point 0 on the graph. Each week, record your weight in the box at the top of the graph and plot the pounds lost on the graph.

After marking your graph each week, take a moment to review your aspirations on the visualization pages for added encouragement.

2 lbs. Avg. Wt. Loss per Wk.

Visualization

As you begin your journey to becoming physically fit, take a moment to visualize how you'll look and feel after you lose weight. Imagine how great it will be to walk by a store window and admire your thinner reflection. The new-found self assurance you'll acquire will help you face each day with greater confidence.

On the following page, write down why you want to lose weight. Be specific—is it because you have to lower your blood pressure? Is that class reunion looming near? Or maybe you simply want to have more years to enjoy your children and grandchildren. Only you know your own personal reasons. Be very open and honest with yourself. Then write down how you imagine you'll look and feel after you get into shape. Your clothes will fit better, you'll be more physically active, and you'll have more confidence in all aspects of your life. What else do you think will happen?

On those days when you need a little extra motivation and you feel more like flopping on the couch with a bag of chips than working out, look back at the visualization pages in your journal. Those aspirations will give you the incentive to toss out the chips, get off the couch, and just do it — because you're worth it!

Why I want to lose weight and become physically fit:

_____

_____

_____

_____

_____

_____

_____

_____

_____

_____

_____

_____

_____

_____

_____

_____

_____

_____

_____

_____

_____

How I expect to look and feel once I'm thinner and healthier:

_____

_____

_____

_____

_____

_____

_____

_____

_____

_____

_____

_____

_____

_____

_____

_____

_____

_____

_____

Behavior Modification

These next pages are important because, as I said in my letter, it has to happen in your mind first. You already are in a good place mentally or you wouldn't be reading this book. So now try to focus on believing that you can be successful. Many emotional factors affect why people overeat or subconsciously make very poor food choices. Boredom, depression, and anger are just a few of the emotions that can prompt you to turn to food for comfort. For some people eating seems to make stressful situations easier to tolerate. This can lead to a lifetime of overeating. It's going to take work to change years of unhealthy learned behavior, but you can do it.

The remedy is to learn new behaviors to deal with stress as well as the joys and disappointments of everyday life. It's much simpler to develop new habits than it is to lose old ones. But with a commitment to establishing healthier behaviors, old habits will fade and be replaced by new ones. Eventually you'll notice a change in the way that you think about food.

The first step is to identify those environmental conditions that trigger your desire to eat. A food journal is an excellent way to do this. By writing down food items, portions, and the emotions that may have triggered an eating response, you will begin to develop an awareness of existing problem areas. Once you identify the pitfalls, you can take steps to correct or replace certain behaviors before reaching for food. Instead of eating, go for a walk, call a friend, take a relaxing soak in the tub, or do something else enjoyable.

Dining out can often present challenges to your good intentions. You may feel that because you're paying for a meal, it's necessary to eat the whole thing ... wrong! That's what "doggie bags" are for. Stop when you're no longer hungry and bring the rest home. Try sharing a meal with your dining companion. Each of you could order a cup of soup and then split an entree. Also, ask your server to bring sauces and dressings on the side and not to bring bread or butter to the table. These simple tips can save you money as well as calories!

Building a support system for yourself is important. It's so helpful to have even one or two other people encourage you by sharing recipes, joining you in physical activity, or cheering you on as you lose weight.

Try incorporating the following behavioral changes into your everyday lifestyle. Just a few small changes can make a big difference!

- Remove high-calorie, high-fat foods from your house.
- Eat slower; put your fork down between bites.
- Switch to skim milk instead of 2% or whole milk.
- Try not to sample food while you're cooking.
- Sit at the table for mealtime; don't eat standing up.
- Don't grocery shop when you're hungry.
- Make a grocery list before shopping and stick to it!
- Keep plenty of healthy foods in plain sight.
- Have desserts but make them "lite."
- Use a smaller plate; it will make your meal appear larger.
- Don't serve "family style." Keep extras in the kitchen.
- Cook without fat. Broil, bake, or poach instead.
- Sample different brands of low-fat, low-calorie foods.
- Be keenly aware of portion sizes.

You'll discover more behaviors that need to be changed as your personal pitfalls reveal themselves on the pages of your journal. Self-recognition is really the key. That's why it's so important to complete a journal page each day and then scrutinize your behavior. You can then prepare yourself to make better choices the next time those negative influences arise.

After you reach your desired weight, keep your journal handy. It will be helpful should you find destructive habits slipping back into your life. Reviewing your journal will help you to refocus on why it was important for you to become fit in the first place. That motivation will get you back on track before things get too far out of hand.

Setting Realistic Goals

Your objective is to set achievable goals that will give you tangible and consistent weekly losses without harming your health. Don't make the mistake of setting unrealistic goals that doom you to fail. It's more satisfying to achieve small goals than to fail at overly ambitious ones. When you lose weight at a slower pace, you're more likely to keep that weight off. If you lose too much too fast, your body will try to fight the loss by slowing down your metabolism.

The more muscular you are, the more efficiently you burn calories. When you reduce your calories below what's believed to be a healthy level (about 1200-1500 calories per day depending upon your size and activity level), you may begin to burn not only stored body fat but muscle as well. That is what you don't want to do.

When you set your calorie and fat gram allowances on the next few pages, keep in mind that in addition to setting an ultimate long-term goal, it's equally important to set several short-term goals. Attaining short-term goals will motivate you to stick with your program. You'll be continually adjusting your food choices until you've established nutritionally sound eating habits that you can live with forever.

Let's face it – what you weighed in high school may no longer be a realistic weight for you! So what should you weigh? There's no magic number but rather a set of guidelines to help you set a healthy goal weight. Ask yourself, what weight have I comfortably maintained as an adult without starving or exercising for hours each day? At what weight do I look and feel my best with energy to spare? The following guidelines will help you determine your healthiest weight.

Body Mass Index

The National Institutes of Health developed this measurement of obesity to assess health risk based on height and weight. It's not necessary to calculate your BMI. We have simply included this page so that you may understand the terminology because it's being used more frequently in the health and fitness industry today.

To determine your Body Mass Index (BMI) multiply your weight in pounds by 704.5 and divide it by your height in inches squared. For example: a 5'2", 140 lb. female has a BMI of 25.6:

$\underline{140 \times 704.5} = \underline{98,630}$

62 x 62 (height in inches, squared) = 3844

98,630 divided by 3844 = 25.6

As BMI increases above 30, health risk and mortality increase significantly.

This measurement does not account for differences in body composition or gender. They are guidelines.

Guidelines are:

BMI of 19 - 24.5 = healthy weight

BMI of 25 - 29.9 = overweight

BMI of > 30 = obese

Waist Circumference:

Where you carry your excess weight matters! Individuals who carry weight around their midsections (centrally) are more apple-shaped and have a greater risk of chronic disease than pear-shaped individuals who carry excess weight around their hips and leg areas.

Measure your waist circumference with a tape measure 1 inch above the navel.

Guidelines are:

Females > 35 inches = overweight

Males > 40 inches = overweight

USDA Guidelines for "Healthy Weight"

In 1995 the USDA developed healthy-weight-for-height charts with wider ranges for males and females, adjusting for age. Consider the midpoint of each range as a realistic goal and allow for a range of 3 pounds to adjust for fluctuations due to fluid shifts. See chart below:

Height (without shoes)	Weight in pounds (without clothes)
5'0"	97-128
5'1"	101-132
5'2"	104-137
5'3"	107-141
5'4"	111-146
5'5"	114-150
5'6"	118-155
5'7"	121-160
5'8"	125-164
5'9"	129-169
5'10"	132-174
5'11"	136-179
6'0"	140-184
6'1"	144-189
6'2"	148-195

Remember: These are guidelines – practically speaking, a person's gender, bone structure or musculature could dictate an ideal weight *slightly* outside of these ranges.

Establishing Calorie Limits

First, the basics... a calorie is a unit of energy; 3,500 of these units (calories) equal one pound of stored body fat. To lose one pound of fat, you'll need to either reduce your caloric intake by 3,500 calories or burn that amount off through additional exercise (or better yet, a combination of the two).

Depending on one's level of activity, the average person requires about 12-15 calories per pound of body weight per day to maintain his or her current weight. For example, a 200 lb. reasonably active man probably consumes about 3,000 calories a day to maintain his weight (200 pounds x 15 calories per pound = 3,000 calories). If that 200 lb. man reduces his calories to 2,500 a day, that 500-calorie reduction for seven days (500 x 7 = 3,500) will result in a one pound weight loss. If he eats 1,000 fewer calories per day, he will lose two pounds in seven days.

Most women lose an average of 1-2 pounds a week by consuming 1,200-1,500 calories a day. Most men lose 1-2 pounds a week by consuming 1,700-2,000 calories a day. A caloric intake below 1,200 calories for women and 1,500 calories for men is not recommended as these diets are often nutritionally inadequate.

If you're accustomed to consuming 3,000 calories a day and you cut back to 2,000 calories, you would lose two pounds per week. A healthy and practical goal would be 1½-2 pounds a week. If you are more than 50 pounds overweight, a 2½-3 pound per week weight loss would not be unreasonable for the first few weeks. On the next page you'll set both your short-term and long-term goals.

Simply stated, to lose:

1 pound a week, reduce your caloric intake by 500 per day.
1-1/2 pounds a week, reduce your caloric intake by 750 per day.
2 pounds a week, reduce your caloric intake by 1000 per day.

Set a realistic 60-day goal. This may or may not be your ultimate goal weight. Then set a one-week goal. Success in attaining short-term goals encourages you to continue on toward your final goal. If you need to lose more weight than is practical in a 60-day period, get another copy of this book and keep on going.

In 60 days I'll lose _____ pounds and I will weigh _____.

In one week I'll lose _____ pounds.

My daily calorie allowance for the next week is _____.

Note: Weigh yourself every week, evaluate your progress, and set a new goal for the next week. Resist the temptation to weigh yourself more frequently, as water retention and other variables will affect your weight on a day-to-day basis. Fixating on numbers may cause you to focus less on your long-term objective.

Establishing Fat Gram Limits

A diet high in fat, especially saturated fat, causes elevated blood cholesterol levels in many people. High blood cholesterol increases your risk of heart disease, the nation's number one killer of both men and women. A high fat intake can also cause obesity, diabetes and certain types of cancer. Reducing dietary fat is a good idea for everyone, especially those limiting calories to reduce weight. Did you know that fat has more than twice the calories of an equal weight of carbohydrates or protein? The fat in food provides many calories but few vitamins or minerals. Reducing fat intake almost always results in fewer calories consumed.

On average, Americans consume about 35% of their total calories as fat. Many health agencies recommend limiting your fat intake to 30% or less of your total calories. Just how much fat is that? Look at the following examples for the amounts of fat that equal 30% of calories.

- Sedentary individuals would normally consume an average of 1,600 calories each day. Each gram of fat contains 9 calories. Thirty percent of calories from fat equals 53 grams (1,600 x .30 = 480, divided by 9 = 53.3, or 53 grams).

- Older children, teenage girls, active women, women who are breast feeding, and many sedentary men consume about 2,200 calories each day. Thirty percent of calories from fat equals 73 grams (2,200 x .30 = 660, divided by 9 = 73.3, or 73 grams).

- Teenage boys, active men, and some very active women consume about 2,800 calories a day. Thirty percent of calories from fat equals 93 fat grams (2,800 x .30 = 840, divided by 9 = 93.3, or 93 fat grams).

Use the following formula to determine your maximum daily limit of fat grams based on the amount of calories you've allowed yourself each day.

$$\underline{\hspace{2cm}} \times 30 = \underline{\hspace{2cm}} \div 9 = \underline{\hspace{2cm}}$$

| Daily calorie | (%) | Calories | Fat gm. |
| Allowance | | per gram | per day |

My daily fat gram allowance for the next week is _____.

The number you've determined as your fat gram allowance should be the maximum amount of fat that you consume per day. If you're able to reduce the percentage of fat in your diet to 25%, all the better.

Note: Once you fully understand where the bad fat comes from and have consistently stayed under your fat gram limit for two weeks, you may then choose to simply track just your calories.

Good Fat, Bad Fat

Most experts agree that a diet lower in saturated fat, trans fatty acids, and cholesterol is a healthier one. Saturated and trans fats have been shown to increase LDL, or "bad" cholesterol levels, and trans fats may even lower HDL, or "good" cholesterol levels. Cholesterol-containing foods may also increase blood cholesterol levels. For every 1% increase in blood cholesterol, there is a 2% increase in the risk of heart disease.

Americans consume an average of 26 grams of saturated fat, 5 grams of trans fat and more than 300 mg of cholesterol each day. A reasonable goal should be to limit saturated fat and trans fats to less than 20 grams, or 6 or 7% of calories, and cholesterol should be limited to less than 250 mg per day. Labels do not yet distinguish between saturated and trans fats, so assume that in most processed foods, trans fat is included in the grams of saturated fat listed. While consuming 30% total fat calories is recommended, it is really the type of fat that has the greatest impact on cholesterol levels.

Sources of Saturated Fat:

Full fat dairy products (whole milk, cheeses, cream, cream cheese, butter)

Prime/ heavily marbled fatty cuts of meat

Poultry skin

Tropical fats (palm, coconut oils)

Lard

Sources of Trans Fat:

Processed snack foods listing "partially hydrogenated" oils as primary ingredients

Snack crackers, chips, cookies

Pastries

Fried foods

Sources of Cholesterol:

Organ meats (liver, sweetbreads)

Egg yolks

Cream-based desserts

Shellfish

Full fat dairy

Fatty meats

The good news is not all fats are bad! In fact, consuming more monounsaturated, polyunsaturated, and omega 3 fats may be beneficial to your health.

Fats and oils actually contain a combination of all three types of fatty acids (saturated, polyunsaturated, monounsaturated) in various proportions. Sources listed indicate the primary fatty acid present.

Sources of Polyunsaturated Fats:

Corn oil

Safflower oil

Soybean oil

Sunflower oil

Liquid oil-based margarines

Sources of Monounsaturated Fats:

Olive oil

Canola oil

Peanut oil

Nut oils

Soybean oil

Sources of Omega 3 fatty acids:

Flaxseed or Flaxseed oil

Higher-fat fish such as salmon, albacore tuna, mackerel, sardines

Fiber Facts

Fiber is a dieter's best friend because it provides a "full" feeling without extra calories. A dict high in fiber can fight obesity, heart disease, diabetes, and cancer. Americans eat an average of 12-17 grams of fiber daily. The American Dietetic Association recommends an intake of 20-35 grams per day.

Fiber occurs in two forms: soluble and insoluble. Both are beneficial.

Soluble Fiber Foods:

Legumes: pinto beans, kidney beans, black beans, peas, lentils

Brans: rice, oat, barley, corn, wheat

Fruits: apples, oranges, pears, peaches, grapes

Vegetables: carrots, potatoes, squash, corn

Whole grain breads and cereals, popcorn

Seeds and nuts

Psyllium seed (found in fiber products like Metamucil)

Insoluble Fiber Foods:

Wheat bran, whole grain breads, crackers, cereals

Whole wheat flour, brown rice

Kidney beans

Skins of fruits such as pears, apples, prunes

Strawberries, boysenberries

Vegetables: green beans, broccoli, peppers,

spinach, carrots, tomatoes, artichokes

Almonds, chunky peanut butter

Exercise - Move It & Lose It!

Besides eating properly, another key ingredient to successful weight loss and maintenance is exercise. Not only does regular physical exercise burn calories, it increases muscle strength and flexibility and strengthens the heart and lungs.

In the past few decades we have seen a proliferation of diet books on the market, such as *The Atkins Diet*, *The Zone*, *Sugar Busters*, *The Carbohydrate Addicts Diet* and *Eat More, Weigh Less*. However, a recent review of popular diets in *Obesity Research* has shown that any diet that creates energy expenditure greater than energy intake will cause weight loss. So, you theoretically could eat a 100% fat diet and lose weight if you were expending more calories than you were consuming. However, we certainly do not recommend it.

There is a great deal of debate in identifying the causes of weight gain and obesity. Experts have demonstrated a correlation between physical inactivity and body weight. Many studies have shown a correlation between a person's weight and the amount of time they spend in sedentary activities, such as watching television. Other experts contend the cause is a combination of calorie-dense food consumption and physical inactivity. The bottom line is that the more active you are, the less likely your chances of gaining unwanted weight.

Before beginning an exercise program you should first see your doctor, especially if you have been inactive, are overweight, smoke, have high blood pressure or high cholesterol levels. Your doctor will help you decide what activity is best for you or if there are any activities that you should avoid.

There are strategies to increase your likelihood of success and help you maintain your new lifestyle. Some effective methods include the "buddy system"– ask a friend or relative to do the program with you; make a written agreement to perform an activity a certain number of days each week for a specified duration; or record activities performed on journal pages and set realistic goals. The biggest key to success is consistency. That is why we've included pages for you to monitor your daily exercise. As you fill in your exercise data and see how many calories you've burned, you'll stay motivated, find that you feel better, and will want to make time for exercise each and every day.

A fitness program that combines aerobic exercise with body strengthening exercise yields optimal results. Aerobic exercise burns calories but does not necessarily build muscle mass. Examples of good aerobic activities include brisk walking, running, cycling, swimming, rowing, stair climbing and cross-country skiing. Strengthening exercise builds muscle mass. The more muscular your body is, the more efficiently it will burn calories. For example, a 200-pound person with a higher percentage of muscle mass is able to consume more calories throughout the day without gaining weight than a 200-pound person whose body composition has a higher percentage of fat. It's not fair, but that's the way it works. Just moving a more muscular body around all day requires more fuel (calories). Muscle operates more effectively than fat. A few strengthening exercises would be weight training and other resistance-type exercises such as push-ups, pull-ups and squats. When starting a weight training program it's a good idea to seek the advice of a fitness trainer. If you do not belong to a health club, seek advice from a health educator at a school or community center.

Make an effort to exercise at least five times a week. A typical workout should last at least 30-60 minutes. Start out slowly if you've been inactive and gradually increase the length of your workout until you reach a minimum of 30 minutes. An aerobic program as simple as brisk walking every other day is a great start. The Surgeon General recommends that every American get 30 or more minutes of moderate activity on most, if not every day of the week.

In addition to the actual exercise you choose, all workouts should include a warm-up, a cool-down and stretching.

Warm-up

The warm-up prepares the body for more vigorous activity. It may include a number of different exercises, but part of the warm-up should be specific to the activity that is about to be performed. For example, brisk walking for 5 to 10 minutes should precede jogging. The warm-up is especially important when it precedes high intensity exercise, such as sprinting. Lack of warm-up can result in a less than satisfactory performance or even injury.

Cool-down

The cool-down allows the body to gradually adjust to diminished activity. During vigorous exercise, blood flow is distributed to the muscles and skin to dissipate heat. Sudden cessation of activity results in the pooling of blood in peripheral muscles and blood vessels. This may cause a sudden drop in blood pressure and fainting. In those individuals with heart disease, either known or unknown, blood flow back to the heart is compromised and the possibility of heart attack is increased.

Stretching

Muscles used during exercise should be stretched. Stretching is best done after exercise for two reasons: the muscles are warm and will attain a greater range of motion with less discomfort; and stretching warm muscles is less likely to result in injury. A stretch should be held for 20 to 30 seconds, to the point of "mild discomfort."

Research has shown that health benefits from activity can be attained by intermittent as well as continuous activity. This information has led to increased use of such devices as step counters and pedometers to encourage walking during the course of daily activity. One very popular program is the 10,000 Step Program, where the goal is to eventually accrue 10,000 steps (about 5 miles) over the course of a day. Increasing physical activity in even small ways, such as taking the stairs instead of the elevator or parking in a spot where you'll have to walk a greater distance, will increase the number of calories you burn. It all adds up. Remember, whether you burn off 3,500 calories through exercise or reduce your caloric intake by 3,500 calories, you will lose one pound. And that, after all, is your objective.

Refer to the Calorie Expenditure chart to see approximately how many calories you can burn when engaging in various types of exercise. These values represent averages. Your weight and muscle density will affect the rate at which you burn calories.

Calorie Expenditure Chart

Activity	Calories per hr.
Aerobics (moderate)	400
Aerobics (intense)	890
Bicycling (leisurely)	250
Bicycling (moderately)	400
Bowling	250
Canoeing	260
Gardening	240
Golf	250
Horseback riding	340
Housework (moderate)	200
Ice skating	380
Jogging (5 mph)	550
Lawn mowing	240
Pilates	320
Racquetball	560
Roller blading	320
Rowing (moderate)	400
Running (8 mph)	780
Skiing (cross-country)	900
Skiing (downhill)	560
Softball	380
Swimming (general)	540
Tennis (doubles)	320
Tennis (singles)	460
Volleyball	370
Walking (fast)	390
Walking (slow)	250
Water aerobics	360
Water-skiing	470
Weight lifting	270
Yoga	230

Average calories – varies by body weight, musculature, and intensity

Exercise Tips

Aerobic Training

Breathing – Before you get started, take a couple of deep breaths, inhale through your nose, hold a few seconds and exhale through your mouth.

Hydration – Drink plenty of fluids (water is best) before, during and after your workout. Keeping the body hydrated allows you to perform the activity more efficiently and reduces the likelihood of side effects such as sideaches and muscle cramps.

Aerobic training zone – To establish the optimum fat-burning range for aerobic activity, use the following formula: Subtract your age from 220, then multiply that number by 85% to arrive at your maximum training heart rate (beats per minute), then multiply that same number by 55% to arrive at your minimum training heart rate.

> i.e., $220 - 55$ (age) $= 165$ x $85\% = 140$ (maximum heart rate)
> $220 - 55$ (age) $= 165$ x $55\% = 91$ (minimum heart rate)
> Target heart range: 91 - 140

To find out what your heart rate is during your workout take your pulse for ten seconds, then multiply that number by 6.

These numbers may be influenced by many factors, including taking heart or high blood pressure medications. Be sure to consult with your physician if you have any existing medical conditions prior to engaging in an exercise program.

Intensity – In the initial stages of your aerobic training stay within the 55-60% heart-rate range. The ideal fat burning range is 65-70%. Higher range numbers are used for cardiovascular efficiency training. Prolonged exercise burns a higher percentage of fat than a short or more intense exercise.

Duration – Begin slow but work up to a minimum of 30 minutes. The reason for this is that initially exercise burns carbohydrates for a few minutes before your body switches from using the glycogen in your muscles to burning the fat as energy. The longer you continue the activity, the more fat you burn. Another benefit is that your body will continue to burn calories more efficiently for an extended period of time after an aerobic workout.

Strength Training

Breathing – Don't hold your breath. Exhale as you exert or lift the weight; inhale as you lower the weight.

Posture – Utilize a draw-in maneuver (tighten your abdominal muscles, drawing belly button inwards to spine). This helps create spinal stabilization, which is important for all exercises. To prevent knee strain, keep your back flat and your knees bent.

Form – Utilize slow, controlled movement patterns as you lift and lower. Remember, **you** control the weight or resistance. The weight shouldn't control you. Produce force up (concentric) for two counts and hold (isometric) for two counts, then reduce force down (eccentric) for four counts.

Frequency – Exercise twice a week at first, progressing to three times a week. Depending on your age and condition, wait 48 to 72 hours between workouts so your muscles will have time to repair and rebuild. A more advanced program (i.e., a split routine) would consist of working two or three muscle groups each day and would require less rest (24 hrs) between workouts, but 48 hrs between working the same muscle group.

Strength Training Variables

Month 1

Frequency	Once or twice a week
Sets	1-3 sets per exercise
Reps	6-8 strength 8-12 development
Volume	10 exercises, 1 set each = 10 total sets
Rest	30-90 seconds = conditioning/circuit training 2-3 minutes = performance/strength
Tempo	2 seconds lift – concentric, 2 seconds hold – isometric, 4 seconds lower – eccentric
Recovery	48-72 hours between strength training of same muscle group. Slightly more time is needed as we get older in order to rebuild and repair. Larger muscle group exercises, i.e., squats or lunges may require more recovery time.

Month 2

Frequency	Two or three times per week
Sets	1-3 sets per exercise
Reps	12-20 endurance (tone)
	10-12 strength/endurance
Volume	10 exercises, 2 sets each = 20 total sets
Rest	Most people will rest about 30-60 seconds between sets.

We have included the following exercise charts to keep track of your strength training and to plan your weekly activities at the beginning of each week. However, it's fine to simply record your daily exercise on each of the 60-day journaling pages.

Psychologically, there are many great benefits to be derived from regular exercise such as favorable changes in brain chemistry, a sense of accomplishment and improved self-esteem.

Be aware that the body adapts to exercise of any type after a given period of time. Therefore, one should vary their exercise type and intensity about every four weeks. This helps to prevent weight loss plateaus.

A final word about exercise: Make it fun. Choose activities that you like to do with people you enjoy. Vary your exercises as much as possible for a more complete workout; this also avoids overworking one particular muscle group. This is called cross training.

Exercise Charts

Weekly Plan:

Mon. _Strength_
Tues. _Cardio_
Wed. _None_
Thurs. _Strength_
Fri. _Cardio_
Sat. _None_
Sun. _Cardio_

STRENGTH TRNG

Exercise	DAY ONE _Mon._			DAY TWO _Thurs._			DAY THREE		
	Set 1 Rep/wt	Set 2 Rep/wt	Set 3 Rep/wt	Set 1 Rep/wt	Set 2 Rep/wt	Set 3 Rep/wt	Set 1 Rep/wt	Set 2 Rep/wt	Set 3 Rep/wt
Bench press	12/80	12/100	12/120	12/80	12/100	12/120			
Lat Row	12/50	12/60	12/70	12/50	12/60	12/70			
Ball Squats	12/50	12/60	12/70	12/50	12/60	12/70			
Shoulder Press	12/60	12/70	12/80	12/60	12/70	12/80			
Bicep Curls	12/35	12/40	12/45	12/35	12/40	12/45			
Tricep Pushdown	12/40	12/45	12/50	12/40	12/45	12/50			
(Add exercises									
when comfortable)									

SAMPLE

CARDIO EXERCISE

		(Space to record additional cardio)
Day One	_Tues._	_Power Walking - 40 minutes_
Day Two	_Fri._	_Biking - 30 minutes_
Day Three	_Sun._	_Aerobics - 45 minutes_
Day Four	___	

WEEK _____

STRENGTH TRNG	DAY ONE _____			DAY TWO _____			DAY THREE _____		
Exercise	Set 1 Rep/wt	Set 2 Rep/wt	Set 3 Rep/wt	Set 1 Rep/wt	Set 2 Rep/wt	Set 3 Rep/wt	Set 1 Rep/wt	Set 2 Rep/wt	Set 3 Rep/wt

Weekly Plan:

Mon. _____
Tues. _____
Wed. _____
Thurs. _____
Fri. _____
Sat. _____
Sun. _____

CARDIO EXERCISE

Day One _____
Day Two _____
Day Three _____
Day Four _____

STRENGTH TRNG	DAY ONE ____						DAY TWO ____						DAY THREE ____					
	Set 1		Set 2		Set 3		Set 1		Set 2		Set 3		Set 1		Set 2		Set 3	
Exercise	Rep/wt		Rep/wt		Rep/wt		Rep/wt		Rep/wt		Rep/wt		Rep/wt		Rep/wt		Rep/wt	

Weekly Plan: ____

Mon. ____

Tues. ____

Wed. ____

Thurs. ____

Fri. ____

Sat. ____

Sun. ____

CARDIO EXERCISE

Day One ____

Day Two ____

Day Three ____

Day Four ____

WEEK _____

Weekly Plan:
Mon. _____
Tues. _____
Wed. _____
Thurs. _____
Fri. _____
Sat. _____
Sun. _____

STRENGTH TRNG	DAY ONE			DAY TWO			DAY THREE		
	Set 1	Set 2	Set 3	Set 1	Set 2	Set 3	Set 1	Set 2	Set 3
Exercise	Rep/wt	Rep/wt	Rep/wt	Rep/wt	Rep/wt	Rep/wt	Rep/wt	Rep/wt	Rep/wt

CARDIO EXERCISE

Day One _____
Day Two _____
Day Three _____
Day Four _____

WEEK _____

Weekly Plan:

Mon. _____
Tues. _____
Wed. _____
Thurs. _____
Fri. _____
Sat. _____
Sun. _____

STRENGTH TRNG	DAY ONE			DAY TWO			DAY THREE		
	Set 1	Set 2	Set 3	Set 1	Set 2	Set 3	Set 1	Set 2	Set 3
Exercise	Rep/wt	Rep/wt	Rep/wt	Rep/wt	Rep/wt	Rep/wt	Rep/wt	Rep/wt	Rep/wt

CARDIO EXERCISE

Day One _____
Day Two _____
Day Three _____
Day Four _____

WEEK _____

STRENGTH TRNG

Exercise	DAY ONE _____			DAY TWO _____			DAY THREE _____		
	Set 1	Set 2	Set 3	Set 1	Set 2	Set 3	Set 1	Set 2	Set 3
	Rep/wt	Rep/wt	Rep/wt	Rep/wt	Rep/wt	Rep/wt	Rep/wt	Rep/wt	Rep/wt

Weekly Plan:

Mon. _____

Tues. _____

Wed. _____

Thurs. _____

Fri. _____

Sat. _____

Sun. _____

CARDIO EXERCISE

Day One _____

Day Two _____

Day Three _____

Day Four _____

WEEK ___

Weekly Plan:

Mon. ___
Tues. ___
Wed. ___
Thurs. ___
Fri. ___
Sat. ___
Sun. ___

STRENGTH TRNG	DAY ONE ___			DAY TWO ___			DAY THREE ___		
	Set 1	Set 2	Set 3	Set 1	Set 2	Set 3	Set 1	Set 2	Set 3
Exercise	Rep/wt	Rep/wt	Rep/wt	Rep/wt	Rep/wt	Rep/wt	Rep/wt	Rep/wt	Rep/wt

CARDIO EXERCISE

Day One ___
Day Two ___
Day Three ___
Day Four ___

WEEK _____

Weekly Plan:

Mon. _____
Tues. _____
Wed. _____
Thurs. _____
Fri. _____
Sat. _____
Sun. _____

STRENGTH TRNG	DAY ONE _____			DAY TWO _____			DAY THREE _____		
	Set 1	Set 2	Set 3	Set 1	Set 2	Set 3	Set 1	Set 2	Set 3
Exercise	Rep/wt	Rep/wt	Rep/wt	Rep/wt	Rep/wt	Rep/wt	Rep/wt	Rep/wt	Rep/wt

CARDIO EXERCISE			
Day One _____			
Day Two _____			
Day Three _____			
Day Four _____			

WEEK _____

STRENGTH TRNG	DAY ONE _____			DAY TWO _____			DAY THREE _____		
	Set 1	Set 2	Set 3	Set 1	Set 2	Set 3	Set 1	Set 2	Set 3
Exercise	Rep/wt	Rep/wt	Rep/wt	Rep/wt	Rep/wt	Rep/wt	Rep/wt	Rep/wt	Rep/wt

Weekly Plan:

Mon. _____
Tues. _____
Wed. _____
Thurs. _____
Fri. _____
Sat. _____
Sun. _____

CARDIO EXERCISE

Day One _____
Day Two _____
Day Three _____
Day Four _____

WEEK _____

STRENGTH TRNG	DAY ONE _____			DAY TWO _____			DAY THREE _____		
	Set 1	Set 2	Set 3	Set 1	Set 2	Set 3	Set 1	Set 2	Set 3
Exercise	Rep/wt	Rep/wt	Rep/wt	Rep/wt	Rep/wt	Rep/wt	Rep/wt	Rep/wt	Rep/wt

Weekly Plan:

Mon. _____

Tues. _____

Wed. _____

Thurs. _____

Fri. _____

Sat. _____

Sun. _____

CARDIO EXERCISE

Day One _____

Day Two _____

Day Three _____

Day Four _____

55

Water—A Drink To Your Health

Last, but certainly not least, you will monitor the amount of water that you drink each day. Drinking at least eight 8-oz. glasses per day is very important for overall health as well as losing weight and keeping it off. Drinking eight or more glasses of water keeps you hydrated and helps every process in the body work better.

When you drink water is almost as important as how much water you drink. Drink a couple of glasses of water one hour before you exercise, and another about 15 minutes before. Continue to stay hydrated during your activity. If you're even slightly dehydrated, you won't be able to perform at your peak. When exercising moderately, it is not as essential but it's still a good idea.

A good time to drink a glass or two of water is about 20 minutes before a meal. You'll tend to eat less because you'll feel the sensation of fullness more quickly. To help keep you on track, the journaling section includes eight boxes for each day. Check-off one box each time you drink an 8-oz. glass of water. These boxes will serve as a reminder to you to drink all eight glasses. Note: The water in coffee, tea, or other drinks does not count toward your eight glasses. Drink eight glasses of pure water in addition to other beverages.

A word about alcohol...

Alcohol beverages pack a caloric punch and actually dehydrate your body. If you drink wine, beer or liquor, alternate a glass of water between each drink. This will slow down your intake of these sneaky calories and will keep you hydrated.

Food Tips

- Space meals throughout the day. Try to eat every four hours to refuel your body and manage your hunger. Record your intake after every meal. If you wait until the end of the day or put it off until tomorrow, you may forget some of what you ate or drank. Writing it down immediately will help you stay aware of your calorie intake for the day.

- Sit and try to do nothing else when you eat. You will be more aware of how much you eat and how satisfied you feel.

- Eat at least five servings of fruits and/or vegetables daily. These foods contain fiber and fluid, which will fill you up with fewer calories. A serving is about the size of a tennis ball. It's better to eat your fruit and vegetables than drink them!

- Try to eat three servings of whole grains daily. Whole grains are higher in fiber and contain disease-fighting nutrients. Examples include 100% whole wheat bread, bagels, muffins, bran cereals, brown rice and popcorn.

- Eat more beans! Legumes or dried beans and peas are loaded with fiber, protein, and B vitamins and are fat-free. Try to eat 1/2-cup servings 2-3 times a week. Examples include lentil or navy bean soup, kidney beans, and garbanzo beans. Throw beans into soups, casseroles or on salads.

- Choose fats wisely. Cut down on animal and dairy fats which can raise cholesterol, and substitute them with monounsaturated (olive oil, canola oil) and polyunsaturated (safflower, corn, or soybean oils) fats in cooking. Eat more heart healthy Omega 3 oils, found in fatty fish (salmon, tuna, mackerel) and flaxseed or flax oil. Also try to limit trans fatty acids found in processed and snack foods.

- Eat sweets or treats with meals or as dessert immediately following your meal. Remember, the first few bites deliver the most satisfaction.

- Slow down and don't overlap bites. Chew one bite at a time and then the next rather than shoving 3 or 4 in at once.

- Stop halfway through your meal, place your hand on your stomach, and ask yourself if you're comfortably satisfied. If so, then stop before you reach that "stuffed" stage.

- Always ask for sauces, dressings, and gravies on the side. Dip your fork into the sauce first and then take a bite and you'll use less than half.

- Shake the salt habit by simply not adding it at the table and using less when you're cooking.

- When recipes call for eggs, use egg substitutes or separate the eggs, using just the egg whites. (You can substitute two egg whites for one egg.)

- When preparing meat or poultry cut off all visible fat and remove the skin. Avoid breading and coating mixes. Bake, broil or grill; don't fry.

- Sampling food while cooking is a hidden pitfall. Keep a dish of sliced fruit or veggies nearby to nibble on or fix a juice spritzer.

- Have a designated eating area–ideally at the table. Only eat when you're in that location. Serve your food on a salad plate; it makes the plate look more full.

- Gradual transitions to low-fat foods and then to non-fat foods can be an effective approach if you're having difficulty making eating changes.

The Food Label

What Does It Really Mean?

Most foods in the grocery store must carry a nutrition label. Look at the "Nutrition Facts" on a product label for specific information on serving size and nutrients, including calories, total fat, saturated fat, cholesterol, and sodium. When determining calorie and fat values from a label, be sure to check the portion size and number of portions in the package. Don't assume a single package contains a single portion!

Nutrient claims like "low fat" can only be used if a food meets legal standards as defined by the U.S. government.

Fat-free   Less than 0.5 grams of fat per serving

Low Fat   3 fat grams or less per serving

Reduced Fat   At least 25% less fat per serving compared to similar food

Cholesterol-free   Less than 2 mg. cholesterol and 2 grams or less saturated fat per serving

Low Cholesterol   20 mg. or less cholesterol and 2 grams or less saturated fat per serving

Portion Primer

Controlling your calorie intake is only as good as your portion accuracy! When you're at home, be sure to measure or weigh items so that you can eyeball portions closely when you're eating out. Ask restaurants about the portion sizes of menu items. To help you estimate portions when you're on the go:

Palm of hand: Women = 3 - 4 oz.
                     Men = 5 - 6 oz.

Tight fist: Women = 1 cup
                     Men = 1 ½ cup

Pinky finger: Women = 1 oz.
                     Men = 1 ½ oz.

Tip of thumb: Women = 1 tsp
                     Men = 2 tsp

If your weight plateaus or you're gaining, take a closer look at your portion sizes.

Now that you're familiar with the various weight loss aspects that you'll be monitoring daily, it's time to start keeping your journal. Whenever possible, look up food values before eating, rather than after, so you can see if you're spending your calories wisely. Be diligent about checking off the water boxes each time you finish a glass of water. Filling in the calories you burn each day through exercise will give you a sense of accomplishment. Most importantly, be candid when writing about emotional influences in the "comments" section of your journal. This way you can recognize where behavioral changes are needed. All of these components, working together, are what it takes to personalize a program for successful weight loss that will work for you. You're on your way to a healthier lifestyle!

My 60-Day Journal

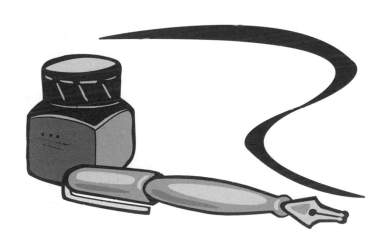

DAY 28

Time & Place	Amt.	Food	Cal.	Bal. 2000	Fat Gm.	Bal. 67
7 a.m.	8 oz.	orange juice	110	1890	0	67
home	1 cup	Special K cereal	110	1780	0	67
	8 oz.	skim milk	90	1690	0	67
	4 slices	turkey bacon	80	1610	2	65
	1 cup	coffee	0	1610	0	65
	1 avg.	bagel	180	1430	2	63
	2 T.	cream cheese (lite)	70	1360	6	57
Noon	1	McChicken sandwich	510	850	30	27
McD.'s	1	garden salad	50	800	2	25
	1 pkg.	vinaigrette (lite)	50	750	2	23
	1 cup	1% milk	100	650	3	20
	1	frozen yogurt sundae	210	440	1	19
5 p.m.	2 oz.	potato chips	300	140	18	1
Mom's	6 oz.	white wine	150	+10	0	1
	6 oz.	pork tenderloin (lean)	280	+290	8	+7
	1/2 cup	carrots	35	+325	0	+7
	1/2 cup	asparagus	20	+345	0	+7
	1 avg.	baked potato	150	+495	0	+7
	2 T.	sour cream (fat-free)	50	+545	0	+7
	1 cup	coffee	0	+545	0	+7
	2 T.	1/2 & 1/2	40	+585	3	+10

SAMPLE

* This is a sample day for a 200-pound person with a weight loss goal of 2 pounds per week. Therefore, this person's daily allowances are 2,000 calories and 67 fat grams. Note: re-adjust calorie and fat gram allowances after each 10-pound weight loss.

Over by 585 calories and 10 fat gms. Get with it!!!

Ending Daily Balances   +585   +10

Today's Exercise	Duration
walked 3 miles (briskly)	_45 minutes_

Calories Burned   _300_

Check one box for each 8-oz. glass of water you drink.

☒ ☒ ☒ ☒ ☒ ☒ ☐ ☐

IT'S WEIGH DAY!

SAMPLE

Starting weight _210_   **Goal weight** _196_

_14_   pounds to lose until I reach my 60-day goal.

What's working? What's not? Revisions?

Drinking more water and adjusting to skim milk—good!
Must look up food values (before) eating! A McGrilled
chicken sandwich would have saved me 26 fat grams &
250 calories! Snacking at Mom's after work is a
problem—visit after dinner! Lots of pressure at work but
the walks help me to unwind. Sure beats eating!

Measurements (for directions, see "My Personal Goals"):

Chest	_45"_	Hips	_41"_
Waist	_42"_	Thighs (optional)	_—_
Abdomen/stomach	_44"_	Other	

My goal is to weigh _208_ **in one week.**

DAY 1

Date: _____

Time & Place	Amt.	Food	Cal.	Bal.	Fat Gm.	Bal.

Ending Daily Balances

Today's Exercise   Duration

_____   _____
_____   _____

Calories Burned _____

Check one box for each 8-oz. glass of water you drink.

☐   ☐   ☐   ☐   ☐   ☐   ☐   ☐

My Personal Goals

Starting weight _____   **60 Day**
                                      Goal weight _____

_____ pounds to lose until I reach my 60-day goal.
A rate of 1-2 pounds lost per week is reasonable.

Changes I will make:

1. _____

2. _____

3. _____

4. _____

5. _____

Measurements (to be taken on Day 1, Day 29, and Day 60):

Chest (taken at fullest part of bust/chest   _____
with arms relaxed at your side)

Waist (taken one inch above navel,   _____
tape straight across back, stomach relaxed)

Abdomen/stomach (taken one inch below   _____
navel, stomach relaxed)

Hips (taken across largest area of buttocks)   _____

Thighs (taken three inches down from groin   _____
 area -- optional)

My goal is to weigh _____ in one week.

DAY
2

Date: _____

Time & Place	Amt.	Food	Cal.	Bal.	Fat Gm.	Bal.
		Ending Daily Balances				

Today's Exercise   Duration

_____   _____

_____   _____

Calories Burned _____ _____

Check one box for each 8-oz. glass of water you drink.

☐   ☐   ☐   ☐   ☐   ☐   ☐   ☐

Comments:

_____

_____

_____

_____

_____

_____

_____

_____

_____

_____

_____

_____

_____

"Whether you think you can or think you can't—you're right."
–Henry Ford

DAY 3

Date: _____

Time & Place	Amt.	Food	Cal.	Bal.	Fat Gm.	Bal.

Ending Daily Balances

Today's Exercise   Duration

_____   _____

_____   _____

Calories Burned _____

Check one box for each 8-oz. glass of water you drink.

☐   ☐   ☐   ☐   ☐   ☐   ☐   ☐

Comments:

_____

_____

_____

_____

_____

_____

_____

_____

_____

_____

_____

_____

_____

_____

*Just as an architect needs a blueprint, you must have an
exercise plan and stick with it.*

DAY
4

Date: _____

Time & Place	Amt.	Food	Cal.	Bal.	Fat Gm.	Bal.
	Ending Daily Balances					

Today's Exercise   Duration

_____   _____

_____   _____

Calories Burned _____

Check one box for each 8-oz. glass of water you drink.

☐   ☐   ☐   ☐   ☐   ☐   ☐   ☐

Comments:

_____

_____

_____

_____

_____

_____

_____

_____

_____

_____

_____

_____

_____

_____

_____

*Keep a support system for yourself. It's great to have
friends join you on a walk or to share low-fat recipes with.*

DAY
5

Date: _____

Time & Place	Amt.	Food	Cal.	Bal.	Fat Gm.	Bal.

Ending Daily Balances

Today's Exercise   Duration

_____   _____

_____   _____

Calories Burned _____ _____

Check one box for each 8-oz. glass of water you drink.

☐   ☐   ☐   ☐   ☐   ☐   ☐   ☐

Comments:

_____

_____

_____

_____

_____

_____

_____

_____

_____

_____

_____

_____

_____

"One can never consent to creep when one feels an impulse to soar."
–Helen Keller

DAY 6

Date: _____

Time & Place	Amt.	Food	Cal.	Bal.	Fat Gm.	Bal.

Ending Daily Balances

Today's Exercise   Duration

_____   _____

_____   _____

Calories Burned   _____   _____

Check one box for each 8-oz. glass of water you drink.

☐   ☐   ☐   ☐   ☐   ☐   ☐   ☐

Comments:

_____

_____

_____

_____

_____

_____

_____

_____

_____

_____

_____

_____

_____

_____

"The man who moves a mountain begins by carrying small stones."
—Chinese proverb

DAY
7

Date: _____

Time & Place	Amt.	Food	Cal.	Bal.	Fat Gm.	Bal.

Ending Daily Balances

Today's Exercise   Duration

_____ ___   _____
_____ ___   _____

Calories Burned ____ _____

Check one box for each 8-oz. glass of water you drink.

□   □   □   □   □   □   □   □

Comments:

_____
_____
_____
_____
_____
_____
_____
_____
_____
_____
_____
_____
_____
_____
_____
_____
_____
_____

*Serve plenty of chilled veggies, fruit, and juices to your
children and grandchildren. This will teach them to
enjoy healthy food choices for a lifetime of fitness.*

DAY
8

Date: _____

Time & Place	Amt.	Food	Cal.	Bal.	Fat Gm.	Bal.

Ending Daily Balances

Today's Exercise   Duration

_____   _____

_____   _____

Calories Burned ___ _____

Check one box for each 8-oz. glass of water you drink.

☐   ☐   ☐   ☐   ☐   ☐   ☐   ☐

IT'S WEIGH DAY!

60-Day
Today's weight _____   **Goal weight** _____
_____ pounds to lose until I reach my 60-day goal.

What's working? What's not? Revisions?

_____

_____

_____

_____

_____

_____

_____

_____

_____

My goal is to weigh _____ **in one week.**

DAY 9

Date: _____

Time & Place	Amt.	Food	Cal.	Bal.	Fat Gm.	Bal.

Ending Daily Balances

Today's Exercise   Duration

_____ ____   _____

_____ ____   _____

Calories Burned __ _____

Check one box for each 8-oz. glass of water you drink.

☐   ☐   ☐   ☐   ☐   ☐   ☐   ☐

Comments:

_____

_____

_____

_____

_____

_____

_____

_____

_____

_____

_____

_____

_____

_____

_____

_____

"Nature does her best to teach us. The more we over-eat, the
harder she makes it for us to get close to the table."
–Earl Wilson

DAY 10

Date: _____

Time & Place	Amt.	Food	Cal.	Bal.	Fat Gm.	Bal.

Ending Daily Balances

Today's Exercise   Duration

_____ ___   _____

_____ ___   _____

Calories Burned __ _____

Check one box for each 8-oz. glass of water you drink.

□   □   □   □   □   □   □   □

Comments:

_____

_____

_____

_____

_____

_____

_____

_____

_____

_____

_____

_____

_____

_____

*The weight reducer is one who has learned that what's on
the table eventually becomes what's on the chair.*

DAY 11

Date: _____

Time & Place	Amt.	Food	Cal.	Bal.	Fat Gm.	Bal.

Ending Daily Balances

Today's Exercise   Duration

_____   _____

_____   _____

Calories Burned _____._____

Check one box for each 8-oz. glass of water you drink.

☐   ☐   ☐   ☐   ☐   ☐   ☐   ☐

Comments:

_____

_____

_____

_____

_____

_____

_____

_____

_____

_____

_____

_____

_____

_____

_____

*Make a grocery list before shopping and stick to it. Never shop when you are
hungry or you are likely to be tempted by enticing displays or packaging.*

DAY
12

Date: _____

Time & Place	Amt.	Food	Cal.	Bal.	Fat Gm.	Bal.

Ending Daily Balances

Today's Exercise   Duration

_____   _____

_____   _____

Calories Burned _____

Check one box for each 8-oz. glass of water you drink.

☐   ☐   ☐   ☐   ☐   ☐   ☐   ☐

Comments:

_____

_____

_____

_____

_____

_____

_____

_____

_____

_____

_____

_____

_____

_____

Steam vegetables to help retain their vitamins.
Try flavoring them with lemon or lime juice instead of butter.

DAY 13

Date: _____

Time & Place	Amt.	Food	Cal.	Bal.	Fat Gm.	Bal.

Ending Daily Balances

Today's Exercise   Duration

_____ ___   _____

_____ ___   _____

Calories Burned _____ _____

Check one box for each 8-oz. glass of water you drink.

☐   ☐   ☐   ☐   ☐   ☐   ☐   ☐

Comments:

_____

_____

_____

_____

_____

_____

_____

_____

_____

_____

_____

_____

_____

_____

If you lose weight quickly, you are likely to gain it back rapidly.
Fad diets do not contain the vitamins and minerals necessary
for good health. Slow and steady works best.

DAY
14

Date: _____

Time & Place	Amt.	Food	Cal.	Bal.	Fat Gm.	Bal.

Ending Daily Balances

Today's Exercise   Duration

_____   ___   _____

_____   _____

Calories Burned ____ _____

Check one box for each 8-oz. glass of water you drink.

☐   ☐   ☐   ☐   ☐   ☐   ☐   ☐

Comments:

_____

_____

_____

_____

_____

_____

_____

_____

_____

_____

_____

_____

_____

_____

*"I don't work-out. If God wanted us to bend over, he'd
put diamonds on the floor."*
–Joan Rivers

DAY 15

Date: _____

Time & Place	Amt.	Food	Cal.	Bal.	Fat Gm.	Bal.

Ending Daily Balances

Today's Exercise   Duration

_____   _____

_____   _____

Calories Burned _____ _____

Check one box for each 8-oz. glass of water you drink.

☐   ☐   ☐   ☐   ☐   ☐   ☐   ☐

IT'S WEIGH DAY!

Today's weight _____   **60-Day**
                                        Goal weight _____

_____ pounds to lose until I reach my 60-day goal.

What's working? What's not? Revisions?

_____

_____

_____

_____

_____

_____

_____

_____

_____

My goal is to weigh _____ **in one week.**

DAY 16

Date: _____

Time & Place	Amt.	Food	Cal.	Bal.	Fat Gm.	Bal.

Ending Daily Balances

Today's Exercise   Duration

_____   _____
_____   _____

Calories Burned ____ _____

Check one box for each 8-oz. glass of water you drink.

☐   ☐   ☐   ☐   ☐   ☐   ☐   ☐

Comments:

_____
_____
_____
_____
_____
_____
_____
_____
_____
_____
_____
_____
_____
_____
_____

Ideal weight: the weight listed on a person's driver's license.

DAY 17

Date: _____

Time & Place	Amt.	Food	Cal.	Bal.	Fat Gm.	Bal.

Ending Daily Balances

Today's Exercise   Duration

_____ ___   _____

_____   _____

Calories Burned ____ _____

Check one box for each 8-oz. glass of water you drink.

☐   ☐   ☐   ☐   ☐   ☐   ☐   ☐

Comments:

_____

_____

_____

_____

_____

_____

_____

_____

_____

_____

_____

_____

_____

_____

Enjoy potato skins? No need to give them up. Coat a cookie sheet with non-fat spray, sprinkle the potato skins or thin slices with garlic salt, pepper and paprika. Broil until crisp.

DAY 18

Date: _____

Time & Place	Amt.	Food	Cal.	Bal.	Fat Gm.	Bal.

Ending Daily Balances

Today's Exercise   Duration

_____ ___   _____

_____ _____   _____

Calories Burned _____ _____

Check one box for each 8-oz. glass of water you drink.

☐   ☐   ☐   ☐   ☐   ☐   ☐   ☐

Comments:

_____

_____

_____

_____

_____

_____

_____

_____

_____

_____

_____

_____

_____

Strawberries dipped in powdered sugar make
a simple, elegant, and fat-free dessert.

DAY 19

Date: _____

Time & Place	Amt.	Food	Cal.	Bal.	Fat Gm.	Bal.

Ending Daily Balances

Today's Exercise   Duration

_____ _____   _____

_____ _____   _____

Calories Burned ___ _____

Check one box for each 8-oz. glass of water you drink.

☐   ☐   ☐   ☐   ☐   ☐   ☐   ☐

Comments:

_____

_____

_____

_____

_____

_____

_____

_____

_____

_____

_____

_____

_____

_____

"If I'd known how long I was going to live,
I'd have taken better care of myself."
–Adolph Zukor at age 99

DAY
20

Date: _____

Time & Place	Amt.	Food	Cal.	Bal.	Fat Gm.	Bal.

Ending Daily Balances

Today's Exercise   Duration

_____   _____

_____   _____

Calories Burned _____ _____

Check one box for each 8-oz. glass of water you drink.

☐   ☐   ☐   ☐   ☐   ☐   ☐   ☐

Comments:

_____

_____

_____

_____

_____

_____

_____

_____

_____

_____

_____

_____

_____

_____

_____

*Add thin-sliced cucumber, tomato, lettuce, or sprouts to your
sandwiches. It makes them more filling and nutritious.*

DAY
21

Date: _____

Time & Place	Amt.	Food	Cal.	Bal.	Fat Gm.	Bal.

Ending Daily Balances

Today's Exercise   Duration

_____   _____

_____   _____

Calories Burned _____

Check one box for each 8-oz. glass of water you drink.

☐   ☐   ☐   ☐   ☐   ☐   ☐   ☐

Comments:

_____

_____

_____

_____

_____

_____

_____

_____

_____

_____

_____

_____

_____

_____

Weight: what a man always loses when his wife is on a diet.

DAY
22

Date: _____

Time & Place	Amt.	Food	Cal.	Bal.	Fat Gm.	Bal.

Ending Daily Balances

108

Today's Exercise   Duration

_____   _____

_____   _____

Calories Burned _____ _____

Check one box for each 8-oz. glass of water you drink.

☐   ☐   ☐   ☐   ☐   ☐   ☐   ☐

IT'S WEIGH DAY!

Today's weight _____   **60-Day
                                     Goal weight** _____
_____ pounds to lose until I reach my 60-day goal.

What's working? What's not? Revisions?

_____

_____

_____

_____

_____

_____

_____

_____

_____

My goal is to weigh _____ in one week.

DAY
23

Date: _____

Time & Place	Amt.	Food	Cal.	Bal.	Fat Gm.	Bal.

Ending Daily Balances

Today's Exercise   Duration

_____   _____
_____   _____

Calories Burned __ _____

Check one box for each 8-oz. glass of water you drink.

☐   ☐   ☐   ☐   ☐   ☐   ☐   ☐

Comments:

_____
_____
_____
_____
_____
_____
_____
_____
_____
_____
_____
_____
_____
_____
_____

"I eat merely to put food out of my mind."
N.F. Simpson

DAY
24

Date: _____

Time & Place	Amt.	Food	Cal.	Bal.	Fat Gm.	Bal.

Ending Daily Balances

Today's Exercise

Duration

_____ _____

_____ _____

Calories Burned _____

Check one box for each 8-oz. glass of water you drink.

☐   ☐   ☐   ☐   ☐   ☐   ☐   ☐

Comments:

_____

_____

_____

_____

_____

_____

_____

_____

_____

_____

_____

_____

_____

_____

_____

Substitute chicken broth, vegetable broth, or white wine for some of the olive oil called for in pesto and other oil-based sauces for pasta.

DAY 25

Date: _____

Time & Place	Amt.	Food	Cal.	Bal.	Fat Gm.	Bal.

Ending Daily Balances

Today's Exercise   Duration

_____   _____

_____   _____

Calories Burned _____

Check one box for each 8-oz. glass of water you drink.

☐   ☐   ☐   ☐   ☐   ☐   ☐   ☐

Comments:

_____

_____

_____

_____

_____

_____

_____

_____

_____

_____

_____

_____

_____

_____

_____

_____

"God must have loved calories because he made so many of them!"
–Anonymous

DAY
26

Date: _____

Time & Place	Amt.	Food	Cal.	Bal.	Fat Gm.	Bal.

Ending Daily Balances

Today's Exercise   Duration

_____   _____

_____   _____

Calories Burned _____

Check one box for each 8-oz. glass of water you drink.

☐   ☐   ☐   ☐   ☐   ☐   ☐   ☐

Comments:

_____

_____

_____

_____

_____

_____

_____

_____

_____

_____

_____

_____

_____

_____

_____

_____

*Reduce cheese in your recipes as much as possible. Cut amounts
called for in half as each ounce contains about 10 grams of fat.*

DAY 27

Date: _____

Time & Place	Amt.	Food	Cal.	Bal.	Fat Gm.	Bal.

Ending Daily Balances

Today's Exercise   Duration

_____   _____

_____   _____

Calories Burned _____

Check one box for each 8-oz. glass of water you drink.

☐   ☐   ☐   ☐   ☐   ☐   ☐   ☐

Comments:

_____

_____

_____

_____

_____

_____

_____

_____

_____

_____

_____

_____

_____

_____

_____

The longer you cook fatty meats, the less fat is left.
When reducing, order your meat medium to well done.

DAY
28

Date: _____

Time & Place	Amt.	Food	Cal.	Bal.	Fat Gm.	Bal.

Ending Daily Balances

Today's Exercise   Duration

_____ _____   _____

_____ _____   _____

Calories Burned _____

Check one box for each 8-oz. glass of water you drink.

☐   ☐   ☐   ☐   ☐   ☐   ☐   ☐

Comments:

_____

_____

_____

_____

_____

_____

_____

_____

_____

_____

_____

_____

_____

_____

_____

_____

Reduce fat in a meatloaf by eliminating the loaf pan.
Place rounded loaves on a broiling pan and bake.
Fat drips through to the lower pan and doesn't stay in the loaf.

DAY 29

Date: _____

Time & Place	Amt.	Food	Cal.	Bal.	Fat Gm.	Bal.

Ending Daily Balances

Today's Exercise   Duration

_____   _____

_____   _____

        Calories Burned   _____

Check one box for each 8-oz. glass of water you drink.

☐   ☐   ☐   ☐   ☐   ☐   ☐   ☐

IT'S WEIGH DAY!

Today's weight _____   **60-Day**
                                       Goal weight _____
_____ pounds to lose until I reach my 60-day goal.

What's working? What's not? Revisions?

_____

_____

_____

_____

_____

_____

Measurements

Chest   _____   Hips   _____
Waist   _____   Thighs (optional)   _____
Abdomen/stomach   _____   Other   _____

        My goal is to weigh _____ **in one week.**

DAY
30

Date: _____

Time & Place	Amt.	Food	Cal.	Bal.	Fat Gm.	Bal.

Ending Daily Balances

Today's Exercise   Duration

_____   _____
_____   _____

Calories Burned ____ _____

Check one box for each 8-oz. glass of water you drink.

☐   ☐   ☐   ☐   ☐   ☐   ☐   ☐

Comments:

_____
_____
_____
_____
_____
_____
_____
_____
_____
_____
_____
_____
_____
_____

"I don't know why I even waste time eating this food.
I should just apply it directly to my hips."
–Rhoda Morgenstern

DAY
31

Date: _____

Time & Place	Amt.	Food	Cal.	Bal.	Fat Gm.	Bal.

Ending Daily Balances

Today's Exercise   Duration

_____   _____

_____   _____

Calories Burned ___ _____

Check one box for each 8-oz. glass of water you drink.
☐   ☐   ☐   ☐   ☐   ☐   ☐   ☐

Comments:

_____

_____

_____

_____

_____

_____

_____

_____

_____

_____

_____

_____

_____

_____

"As a child, my family's menu consisted of two choices- -take it or leave it."
–Buddy Hackett

DAY
32

Date: _____

Time & Place	Amt.	Food	Cal.	Bal.	Fat Gm.	Bal.

Ending Daily Balances

Today's Exercise   Duration

_____ _____   _____

_____   _____

Calories Burned _____

Check one box for each 8-oz. glass of water you drink.

☐   ☐   ☐   ☐   ☐   ☐   ☐   ☐

Comments:

_____

_____

_____

_____

_____

_____

_____

_____

_____

_____

_____

_____

_____

_____

_____

*Eat according to your body signals. Getting overly hungry just
sets you up to over-eat when you finally have a meal.*

DAY 33

Date: _____

Time & Place	Amt.	Food	Cal.	Bal.	Fat Gm.	Bal.

Ending Daily Balances

Today's Exercise   Duration

_____   _____

_____   _____

Calories Burned _____

Check one box for each 8-oz. glass of water you drink.

☐   ☐   ☐   ☐   ☐   ☐   ☐   ☐

Comments:

_____

_____

_____

_____

_____

_____

_____

_____

_____

_____

_____

_____

_____

_____

*Vary the types of exercises you do; this will encompass
more muscles and prevent you from becoming bored.*

DAY
34

Date: _____

Time & Place	Amt.	Food	Cal.	Bal.	Fat Gm.	Bal.

Ending Daily Balances

Today's Exercise   Duration

_____   _____

_____   _____

Calories Burned __ _____

Check one box for each 8-oz. glass of water you drink.

☐   ☐   ☐   ☐   ☐   ☐   ☐   ☐

Comments:

_____

_____

_____

_____

_____

_____

_____

_____

_____

_____

_____

_____

_____

_____

"Oh Lord, if you can't make me look thin, then please make my friends look fat."
- Erma Bombeck

DAY 35

Date: _____

Time & Place	Amt.	Food	Cal.	Bal.	Fat Gm.	Bal.

Ending Daily Balances

Today's Exercise   Duration

_____   _____

_____   _____

Calories Burned _____

Check one box for each 8-oz. glass of water you drink.

☐   ☐   ☐   ☐   ☐   ☐   ☐   ☐

Comments:

_____

_____

_____

_____

_____

_____

_____

_____

_____

_____

_____

_____

_____

_____

_____

For a low-fat, tasty baked potato topping, try salsa.
It's surprisingly good!

DAY 36

Date: _____

Time & Place	Amt.	Food	Cal.	Bal.	Fat Gm.	Bal.

Ending Daily Balances

Today's Exercise   Duration

_____   _____

_____   _____

Calories Burned _____

Check one box for each 8-oz. glass of water you drink.

☐   ☐   ☐   ☐   ☐   ☐   ☐   ☐

IT'S WEIGH DAY!

60-Day
Today's weight _____   **Goal weight** _____
_____ pounds to lose until I reach my 60-day goal.

What's working? What's not? Revisions?

_____

_____

_____

_____

_____

_____

_____

_____

_____

My goal is to weigh _____ **in one week.**

DAY
37

Date: _____

Time & Place	Amt.	Food	Cal.	Bal.	Fat Gm.	Bal.

Ending Daily Balances

Today's Exercise   Duration

_____   _____

_____   _____

Calories Burned _____

Check one box for each 8-oz. glass of water you drink.

☐   ☐   ☐   ☐   ☐   ☐   ☐   ☐

Comments:

_____

_____

_____

_____

_____

_____

_____

_____

_____

_____

_____

_____

_____

_____

_____

Whenever possible keep fruits, vegetables or bagels in a
small cooler and take them with you each day. When healthy
foods are available, you will be less likely to buy junk food.

DAY
38

Date: _____

Time & Place	Amt.	Food	Cal.	Bal.	Fat Gm.	Bal.

Ending Daily Balances

Today's Exercise   Duration

_____ _____   _____

_____   _____

Calories Burned _____

Check one box for each 8-oz. glass of water you drink.

☐   ☐   ☐   ☐   ☐   ☐   ☐   ☐

Comments:

_____

_____

_____

_____

_____

_____

_____

_____

_____

_____

_____

_____

_____

_____

_____

_____

Obstacles are things people see when they take their eyes off a goal.

DAY 39

Date: _____

Time & Place	Amt.	Food	Cal.	Bal.	Fat Gm.	Bal.

Ending Daily Balances

Today's Exercise   Duration

_____   _____   _____

_____   _____

Calories Burned _____

Check one box for each 8-oz. glass of water you drink.

☐   ☐   ☐   ☐   ☐   ☐   ☐   ☐

Comments:

_____

_____

_____

_____

_____

_____

_____

_____

_____

_____

_____

_____

_____

_____

*Walking a mile will burn as many calories as jogging a mile
and will put much less pressure on your joints.*

DAY 40

Date: _____

Time & Place	Amt.	Food	Cal.	Bal.	Fat Gm.	Bal.

Ending Daily Balances

Today's Exercise   Duration

_____   _____

_____   _____

Calories Burned _____

Check one box for each 8-oz. glass of water you drink.

☐   ☐   ☐   ☐   ☐   ☐   ☐   ☐

Comments:

_____

_____

_____

_____

_____

_____

_____

_____

_____

_____

_____

_____

_____

_____

_____

*"The trouble with jogging is by the time you realize you're
not in shape for it, it's too far to walk back."*
–Franklin P. Jones

DAY
41

Date: _____

Time & Place	Amt.	Food	Cal.	Bal.	Fat Gm.	Bal.

Ending Daily Balances

Today's Exercise   Duration

_____   _____

_____   _____

Calories Burned _____

Check one box for each 8-oz. glass of water you drink.

☐   ☐   ☐   ☐   ☐   ☐   ☐   ☐

Comments:

_____

_____

_____

_____

_____

_____

_____

_____

_____

_____

_____

_____

_____

_____

Use lettuce leaves instead of a tortilla for a tasty, low-calorie burrito. Fill them with meat, low-fat cheese, veggies, and salsa.

DAY 42

Date: _____

Time & Place	Amt.	Food	Cal.	Bal.	Fat Gm.	Bal.

Ending Daily Balances

Today's Exercise   Duration

_____   _____

_____   _____

Calories Burned _____

Check one box for each 8-oz. glass of water you drink.

☐   ☐   ☐   ☐   ☐   ☐   ☐   ☐

Comments:

_____

_____

_____

_____

_____

_____

_____

_____

_____

_____

_____

_____

_____

_____

*"You know you've lost too much weight when panhandlers
give you money and tell you to get a hot meal."*
–Anonymous

DAY
43

Date: _____

Time & Place	Amt.	Food	Cal.	Bal.	Fat Gm.	Bal.

Ending Daily Balances

Today's Exercise   Duration

_____   _____

_____   _____

Calories Burned _____

Check one box for each 8-oz. glass of water you drink.

☐   ☐   ☐   ☐   ☐   ☐   ☐   ☐

IT'S WEIGH DAY!

Today's weight _____   **60-Day Goal weight** _____

_____ pounds to lose until I reach my 60-day goal.

What's working? What's not? Revisions?

_____

_____

_____

_____

_____

_____

_____

_____

_____

My goal is to weigh _____ **in one week.**

DAY
44

Date: _____

Time & Place	Amt.	Food	Cal.	Bal.	Fat Gm.	Bal.

Ending Daily Balances

Today's Exercise   Duration

_____   _____

_____   _____

Calories Burned _____

Check one box for each 8-oz. glass of water you drink.

☐   ☐   ☐   ☐   ☐   ☐   ☐   ☐

Comments:

_____

_____

_____

_____

_____

_____

_____

_____

_____

_____

_____

_____

_____

_____

"My wife is a light eater. As soon as it's light, she starts eating."
–Henny Youngman

DAY
45

Date: _____

Time & Place	Amt.	Food	Cal.	Bal.	Fat Gm.	Bal.

Ending Daily Balances

Today's Exercise   Duration

_____   _____

_____   _____

Calories Burned _____

Check one box for each 8-oz. glass of water you drink.

☐   ☐   ☐   ☐   ☐   ☐   ☐   ☐

Comments:

_____

_____

_____

_____

_____

_____

_____

_____

_____

_____

_____

_____

_____

_____

*It's best not to serve meals "family-style." Putting food in bowls on
the table tempts you to reach for second helpings.*

DAY 46

Date: _____

Time & Place	Amt.	Food	Cal.	Bal.	Fat Gm.	Bal.

Ending Daily Balances

Today's Exercise   Duration

_____   _____
_____   _____

Calories Burned _____

Check one box for each 8-oz. glass of water you drink.

☐   ☐   ☐   ☐   ☐   ☐   ☐   ☐

Comments:

_____
_____
_____
_____
_____
_____
_____
_____
_____
_____
_____
_____
_____
_____

*My aunt knew she was in trouble when she went to the
department store and told the clerk, "I'd like to see a
bathing suit in my size," and the clerk replied, "So would I."*

DAY
47

Date: _____

Time & Place	Amt.	Food	Cal.	Bal.	Fat Gm.	Bal.

Ending Daily Balances

Today's Exercise   Duration

_____ _____   _____

_____   _____

Calories Burned _____

Check one box for each 8-oz. glass of water you drink.

☐   ☐   ☐   ☐   ☐   ☐   ☐   ☐

Comments:

_____

_____

_____

_____

_____

_____

_____

_____

_____

_____

_____

_____

_____

_____

_____

*"Once during Prohibition, I was forced to live on
nothing but food and water for several days."*
–W.C. Fields

DAY 48

Date: _____

Time & Place	Amt.	Food	Cal.	Bal.	Fat Gm.	Bal.

Ending Daily Balances

Today's Exercise   Duration

_____   _____
_____   _____

Calories Burned _____

Check one box for each 8-oz. glass of water you drink.

☐   ☐   ☐   ☐   ☐   ☐   ☐   ☐

Comments:

_____
_____
_____
_____
_____
_____
_____
_____
_____
_____
_____
_____
_____
_____
_____
_____

"The only reason I would take up jogging is so that
I could hear heavy breathing again."
–Erma Bombeck

DAY
49

Date: _____

Time & Place	Amt.	Food	Cal.	Bal.	Fat Gm.	Bal.

Ending Daily Balances

Today's Exercise   Duration

_____ ___   _____
_____   _____

Calories Burned ____ _____

Check one box for each 8-oz. glass of water you drink.

☐   ☐   ☐   ☐   ☐   ☐   ☐   ☐

Comments:

_____

_____

_____

_____

_____

_____

_____

_____

_____

_____

_____

_____

_____

"I knew it was time to slow down on my eating when
I started putting whipped cream on my vitamin pills."
–Jackie Gleason

DAY
50

Date: _____

Time & Place	Amt.	Food	Cal.	Bal.	Fat Gm.	Bal.

Ending Daily Balances

Today's Exercise   Duration

_____   _____

_____   _____

Calories Burned ____ _____

Check one box for each 8-oz. glass of water you drink.

☐   ☐   ☐   ☐   ☐   ☐   ☐   ☐

IT'S WEIGH DAY!

Today's weight _____   **60-Day**
                              Goal weight _____

_____ pounds to lose until I reach my 60-day goal.

What's working? What's not? Revisions?

_____ _____

_____ _____

_____

_____

_____

_____

__ _____

_____

_____ _____

My goal is to weigh _____ in one week.

DAY
51

Date: _____

Time & Place	Amt.	Food	Cal.	Bal.	Fat Gm.	Bal.

Ending Daily Balances

Today's Exercise   Duration

_____   _____
_____   _____

Calories Burned _____

Check one box for each 8-oz. glass of water you drink.

☐   ☐   ☐   ☐   ☐   ☐   ☐   ☐

Comments:

_____
_____
_____
_____
_____
_____
_____
_____
_____
_____
_____
_____
_____
_____

*"You know it's time to diet when you fall down and
rock yourself to sleep trying to get up."*
—Anonymous

DAY
52

Date: _____

Time & Place	Amt.	Food	Cal.	Bal.	Fat Gm.	Bal.
		Ending Daily Balances				

Today's Exercise   Duration

_____ _____   _____
_____   _____

Calories Burned _____

Check one box for each 8-oz. glass of water you drink.
☐   ☐   ☐   ☐   ☐   ☐   ☐   ☐

Comments:

_____
_____
_____
_____
_____
_____
_____
_____
_____
_____
_____
_____
_____
_____

"Quit worrying about your health –eventually it will go away."
–Anonymous

DAY
53

Date: _____

Time & Place	Amt.	Food	Cal.	Bal.	Fat Gm.	Bal.

Ending Daily Balances

Today's Exercise   Duration

_____   _____

_____   _____

Calories Burned _____

Check one box for each 8-oz. glass of water you drink.

☐   ☐   ☐   ☐   ☐   ☐   ☐   ☐

Comments:

_____

_____

_____

_____

_____

_____

_____

_____

_____

_____

_____

_____

_____

_____

_____

"Conscience is the small voice that keeps interrupting when food is talking."
—Anonymous

DAY
54

Date: _____

Time & Place	Amt.	Food	Cal.	Bal.	Fat Gm.	Bal.

Ending Daily Balances

Today's Exercise   Duration

_____   _____   _____

_____   _____   _____

Calories Burned _____

Check one box for each 8-oz. glass of water you drink.

☐   ☐   ☐   ☐   ☐   ☐   ☐   ☐

Comments:

_____

_____

_____

_____

_____

_____

_____

_____

_____

_____

_____

_____

_____

_____

Adding club soda to fruit juices adds sparkle,
makes them go farther, and reduces calories per portion.

DAY
55

Date: _____

Time & Place	Amt.	Food	Cal.	Bal.	Fat Gm.	Bal.

Ending Daily Balances

Today's Exercise   Duration

_____   _____
_____   _____

Calories Burned _____

Check one box for each 8-oz. glass of water you drink.

☐   ☐   ☐   ☐   ☐   ☐   ☐   ☐

Comments:

_____
_____
_____
_____
_____
_____
_____
_____
_____
_____
_____
_____
_____
_____
_____
_____

"I'm on a seafood diet. Every time I see food, I eat it."
—Anonymous

DAY 56

Date: _____

Time & Place	Amt.	Food	Cal.	Bal.	Fat Gm.	Bal.

Ending Daily Balances

Today's Exercise   Duration

_____   _____

_____   _____

Calories Burned _____

Check one box for each 8-oz. glass of water you drink.

☐   ☐   ☐   ☐   ☐   ☐   ☐   ☐

Comments:

_____

_____

_____

_____

_____

_____

_____

_____

_____

_____

_____

_____

_____

_____

_____

Keep higher calorie foods in the back of the refrigerator or on the top cupboard shelf. Store healthier items where they are more accessible.

DAY
57

Date: _____

Time & Place	Amt.	Food	Cal.	Bal.	Fat Gm.	Bal.

Ending Daily Balances

Today's Exercise   Duration

_____   _____

_____   _____

Calories Burned _____

Check one box for each 8-oz. glass of water you drink.

☐   ☐   ☐   ☐   ☐   ☐   ☐   ☐

IT'S WEIGH DAY!

60-Day
Today's weight _____   **Goal weight** _____
_____ pounds to lose until I reach my 60-day goal.

What's working? What's not? Revisions?

_____

_____

_____

_____

_____

_____

_____

_____

_____

Just three more days to go!

DAY
58

Date: _____

Time & Place	Amt.	Food	Cal.	Bal.	Fat Gm.	Bal.

Ending Daily Balances

Today's Exercise   Duration

_____ _____   _____

_____ _____   _____

Calories Burned _____

Check one box for each 8-oz. glass of water you drink.

☐   ☐   ☐   ☐   ☐   ☐   ☐   ☐

Comments:

_____

_____

_____

_____

_____

_____

_____

_____

_____

_____

_____

_____

_____

_____

*Expand your horizons—make a point of trying
a new fruit or vegetable each week.*

DAY 59

Date: _____

Time & Place	Amt.	Food	Cal.	Bal.	Fat Gm.	Bal.

Ending Daily Balances

Today's Exercise   Duration

_____   _____

_____   _____

Calories Burned _ _____

Check one box for each 8-oz. glass of water you drink.

☐   ☐   ☐   ☐   ☐   ☐   ☐   ☐

Comments:

_____

_____

_____

_____

_____

_____

_____

_____

_____

_____

_____

_____

_____

_____

*Another great reducing exercise: shake your head vigorously
from side to side when offered a second helping.*

DAY 60

Date: _____

Time & Place	Amt.	Food	Cal.	Bal.	Fat Gm.	Bal.

Ending Daily Balances

Today's Exercise   Duration

_____   _____

_____   _____

Calories Burned _____

Check one box for each 8-oz. glass of water you drink.

☐   ☐   ☐   ☐   ☐   ☐   ☐   ☐

FINAL WEIGH DAY!

Starting weight _____   **Today's weight** _____

I lost _____ **pounds!**

Measurements   **Total inches lost**

Chest   _____   _____

Waist   _____   _____

Abdomen/stomach   _____   _____

Hips   _____   _____

Thighs (optional) _____   _____

Other   _____   _____

Congratulations on a job well-done!

You can be proud of your accomplishment! If you have more
weight to lose, start another book and continue charting as you
have been until you reach your ultimate goal. On the following
page review your past 60-day experience.

Describe the various problems that you encountered the past two months and the solutions you found to combat them. Write down how your emotions influenced your eating habits in the past and how you have learned to modify your responses to them in a healthier manner. What motivated you to stick with your regular exercise program? How do you feel differently about yourself? Do others respond differently to you? How has your health improved? What can you do now that you couldn't do before? Reviewing all of the positive changes that resulted from your weight loss will motivate you to get back on track if destructive eating habits begin to reappear. If you have additional weight to lose, simply pick up another copy of this book and continue the program until you reach your goal.

_____

_____

_____

_____

_____

_____

_____

_____

_____

_____

_____

_____

_____

_____

Nutritional Values

Including Fast Foods!

Let Your Conscience Be Your Guide!

Nutritional Information

Food Item	Amount	Fat Gm.	Calories
Alcohol			
Beer			
regular	12 fl. oz.	0	150
light	12 fl. oz.	0	100
Champagne	6 fl. oz.	0	110
Cordials			
Amaretto	1 fl. oz.	0	100
Brandy (fruit flavored)	1 fl. oz.	0	95
Creme de Menthe	1 fl. oz.	0	125
Drambuie	1 fl. oz.	0	125
Peppermint Schnapps	1 fl. oz.	0	85
Southern Comfort	1 fl. oz.	0	120
Triple Sec	1 fl. oz.	0	80
Liquor, distilled (Note: the higher the proof, the higher the calories)			
80 proof	1 fl. oz.	0	65
86 proof	1 fl. oz.	0	70
90 proof	1 fl. oz.	0	75
94 proof	1 fl. oz.	0	80
100 proof	1 fl. oz.	0	85
Malt liquor	12 fl. oz.	0	190
Wine			
Burgundy	6 fl. oz.	0	130
Chablis	6 fl. oz.	0	120
Chardonnay	6 fl. oz.	0	120
Rosé	6 fl. oz.	0	130
Table wine, sweet	6 fl. oz.	0	270
White Zinfandel	6 fl. oz.	0	125
Wine cooler	8 fl. oz.	0	85
Beverages			
Club Soda	12 fl. oz.	0	0
Cocoa			
w/ skim milk	8 fl. oz.	2	160
w/ whole milk	8 fl. oz.	9	220
mix, no added sugar	1 serving	0	50
Coffee, brewed	8 fl. oz.	0	0
Coffee, flavored mixes, instant	6 fl. oz.	2	55
Crystal Light	8 fl. oz.	0	5
Eggnog	8 fl. oz.	20	350
Espresso Drinks			
Espresso	2 fl. oz.	0	2
Cappuccino, nonfat	12 fl. oz.	1	100
Latte, nonfat	12 fl. oz.	0	120
Mocha	12 fl. oz.	11	280
Frappuccino, regular	1 bottle	3	190

Food Item	Amount	Fat Gm.	Calories
Fruitopia, all flavors	8 fl. oz.	0	120
Gatorade	12 fl. oz.	0	90
Grape juice, canned	6 fl. oz.	0	120
Kool-Aid	8 fl. oz.	0	95
Lemonade	8 fl. oz.	0	100
Orange Juice, unswtnd	8 fl. oz.	0	110
Snapple			
iced tea	8 fl. oz.	0	110
lemonade	8 fl. oz.	0	110
Soft Drinks			
regular	12 fl. oz.	0	160
sugar-free	12 fl. oz.	0	0
Tang	8 fl. oz.	0	120
Tea 8 fl. oz.	0	0	
Country Time Tea	8 fl. oz.	0	70
Breads			
Bagel, plain	1 average	2	180
Biscuit			
baking powder	1 medium	7	160
buttermilk	1 medium	5	100
from mix	1 medium	4	120
Bisquick	1 cup	17	510
Bisquick, reduced fat	1 cup	8	450
Boboli shell	1/2	3	160
Breadsticks			
plain	1 stick	0	25
sesame	1 stick	4	30
Bread			
buttermilk	1 slice	1	70
French	1 slice	1	70
fruit	1 slice	3	120
honey wheat	1 slice	1	70
Italian	1 slice	1	80
"lite" varieties	1 slice	1	40
multi-grain	1 slice	1	70
pita, plain	1 large	1	240
pita, whole wheat	1 large	1	200
raisin	1 slice	1	70
Roman Meal	1 slice	1	70
rye, American	1 slice	1	70
rye, pumpernickel	1 slice	1	80
sourdough	1 slice	1	70
white, enriched	1 slice	1	70
whole wheat	1 slice	1	60
bread crumbs, dry	1 cup	5	400

Nutritional Information

Food Item	Amount	Fat Gm.	Calories
Breads (continued)			
Coffee cake	1 piece	8	220
Cornbread	1 slice	8	200
Cornmeal	1 cup	2	500
Cornstarch	1T	0	35
Crackers			
cheese	5 pieces	5	80
Cheese Nips	10 crackers	3	60
cheese w/peanut butter	2 oz. pkg.	13	280
Goldfish	15 crackers	2	40
graham	4 squares	2	120
graham, low fat	12 squares	2	165
Harvest Wheats	5 crackers	4	90
Hi Ho	5 crackers	5	100
melba toast	1 piece	0	15
oyster	20 crackers	2	80
rice cakes	1 cake	0	35
Ritz	5 crackers	5	85
Ritz, reduced fat	8 crackers	4	110
Ritz Bits	23 pieces	5	85
Rye Krisp	2 crackers	0	50
Saltines	2 crackers	1	26
Fat-free saltines	5 crackers	0	50
Snackwell Wheat	5 crackers	0	60
Sociables	6 crackers	3	70
Soda	6 crackers	2	50
Triscuit	3 crackers	2	65
Triscuit, reduced fat	4 crackers	2	65
Wasa crispbread	1 piece	1	45
Waverly Wafers	3 crackers	2	50
Wheat Thins	5 crackers	2	45
Wheat Thins, red. fat	18 crackers	3	130
Wheatsworth	5 crackers	3	70
Zwieback	3 crackers	1	60
Crepe	1 large	2	60
Croissant	1 medium	11	160
Croutons	1/4 cup	2	45
Danish	1 medium	20	250
Doughnut, cake	1 average	18	250
Doughnut, Krispy Creme	1	11	200
Doughnut, Glazed/Raised	1	14	240
English muffin	1	1	135
Flour			
rice	1 cup	1	430
soy	1 cup	18	380
white	1 cup	1	400
white, all purpose	1 cup	1	420

Food Item	Amount	Fat Gm.	Calories
whole wheat	1 cup	2	400
French toast			
frozen	1 slice	6	140
homemade	1 slice	10	170
Hushpuppy	1 average	11	150
Matzo ball	1	8	125
Matzo	1 board	4	110
Muffins, most varieties	1 large	15	300
banana nut	1 medium	5	135
Betty Crocker, fat-free	1 medium	0	110
blueberry, from mix	1 medium	4	125
bran, homemade	1 medium	5	110
corn	1 medium	4	130
Krusteaz,			
fat-free blueberry	1 medium	0	130
Pancakes			
blueberry, (mix)	3 medium	15	320
buckwheat (mix)	3 medium	12	270
buttermilk (mix)	3 medium	10	270
homemade	3 medium	10	300
"lite" (mix)	3 medium	2	130
Popover	1	5	170
Pop-tarts, mini, frosted choc	1 pouch	4	170
Pop-tarts, low fat	1	3	190
Rolls			
brown & serve	1	2	90
cloverleaf	1	3	90
crescent	1	6	100
croissant	1 medium	8	135
French	1	1	140
hamburger	1	3	180
hard	1	1	120
hotdog	1	2	120
kaiser/hoagie	1 large	2	180
parkerhouse	1	2	60
rye	1	2	55
sesame seed	1	2	60
submarine	1 large	5	400
wheat	1	2	60
white	1	2	110
white, homemade	1	3	120
whole wheat	1	1	85
Scone	1	6	130
Soft bread stick	1	1	130
Stuffing			
bread, mix	1/2 cup	12	200
corn bread, mix	1/2 cup	5	175

Nutritional Information

Food Item	Amount	Fat Gm.	Calories	Food Item	Amount	Fat Gm.	Calories
Breads (continued)				Chocolate chips			
Stove Top	1/2 cup	9	175	Hershey's reduced fat	1 oz.	7	120
Sweet roll, iced	1 medium	8	200	Milk chocolate	1/4 cup	11	220
Tortilla				Semi-sweet	1/4 cup	12	220
corn, 8"	1	3	70	Chocolate-covered cherries	1 oz.	5	125
flour, 8"	1	5	90	Chocolate-covered crm center	1 oz.	5	125
Turnover, fruit filled	1	20	225	Chocolate-covered peanuts	1 oz.	12	160
Waffle				Chocolate covered raisins	1 oz.	5	120
frozen	1 medium	4	100	Chocolate, gourmet dark	1 oz.	10	145
frozen, Aunt Jemima low fat	2	1	160	Candy Kisses	6 pieces	9	150
homemade	1 large	13	245	Chocolate Stars	6 pieces	7	140
Candy				English Toffee	1 oz.	3	110
Butterscotch	8 pieces	3	140	Fudge w/marshmallows	1 oz.	2	90
Butterscotch chips	1 oz.	7	230	Fudge w/o nuts	1 oz.	3	110
Candied fruit	1 oz.	0	90	Fudge w/nuts	1 oz.	5	120
Candy bars				Good & Plenty	1 oz.	0	105
Almond Joy	1 oz.	8	130	Gumdrops	30	0	100
Baby Ruth	1 oz.	7	140	Hard candy	5 pieces	0	100
Bit-o-Honey	1 oz.	2	120	Jelly beans	1 oz.	0	100
Butterfinger	1 oz.	6	130	Licorice	1 oz.	0	35
Chunky, milk chocolate	1 oz.	4	120	Life Savers	6	0	50
Chunky, original	1 oz.	7	140	M&Ms, plain	1 oz.	6	130
Crunch'n Munch, reduced fat	1 cup	4	210	M&Ms, peanut	1 oz.	8	145
Golden Almond, Hershey	1 oz.	11	150	Malted milk balls	1 oz.	7	140
Heath Bar	1 oz.	9	150	Marshmallow	1	0	25
Kit Kat	1 oz.	8	150	Mints	20	1	150
Krackle, Hershey	1 oz.	7	135	Peanut brittle	1 oz.	9	150
Mars	1 oz.	7	135	Reese's Peanut Butter Cup	1	9	150
Milk chocolate, w/almonds	1 oz.	10	150	Sugar Daddy	1 oz.	1	150
Milk chocolate, Hershey	1 oz.	9	150	Taffy	1 oz.	1	100
Milk chocolate, Nestle	1 oz.	9	145	Tootsie Roll	1 oz.	2	110
Milky Way	1 oz.	4	120	**Cereals**			
Milky Way Lite	1.57 oz.	5	170	All Bran	1 cup	1	215
Mounds	1 oz.	7	130	Alpha-Bits	1 cup	1	110
Mr. Goodbar	1 oz.	11	155	Apple Jacks	1 cup	0	110
Nestle's Crunch	1 oz.	8	150	Bran Buds	1 cup	2	200
Peppermint patty, York	1.5 oz.	4	170	Bran Chex	1 cup	1	135
Snickers	1 oz.	7	135	Bran Flakes 40%	1 cup	1	125
Special Dark, Hershey	1 oz.	9	150	Bran, 100%	1 cup	4	200
Three Musketeers	1 oz.	4	140	Brown Sugar Sq., Healthy Choice	1 cup	1	155
Twix	1 oz.	7	140	Cheerios	1 cup	2	90
Cadbury Crème Eggs	1 oz.	6	140	Corn Chex	1 cup	0	110
Candy-coated almonds	1 oz.	5	130	Cornflakes	1 cup	0	110
Caramel corn	1 cup	7	150	Cracklin Oat Bran	1 cup	8	200
Caramel corn w/o nuts	1 oz.	6	115	Cream of Wheat	1 cup	0	140
				Fiber One	1 cup	2	130

Nutritional Information

Food Item	Amount	Fat Gm.	Calories	Food Item	Amount	Fat Gm.	Calories
Cereals(continued)				Cheddar, reduced fat	1 oz.	6	90
Fruit Loops	1 cup	0	110	Cheese food, cold pack	2 T	8	95
Fruit & Fiber				Cheese sauce	1/2 cup	20	260
w/ apples & cinnamon	1 cup	0	180	Cheese spread, Kraft	1 oz.	6	80
w/ dts., rsn., & Wlnts.	1 cup	2	180	Cheez Whiz	1 oz.	6	80
Golden Grahams	1 cup	1	135	Colby	1 oz.	9	110
Granola	1 cup	15	400	Cottage Cheese			
Kellogg's low fat granola	1 cup	6	360	fat-free	1/2 cup	0	90
Grapenut Flakes	1 cup	0	115	1% fat	1/2 cup	1	80
Grape-nuts	1/2 cup	1	210	2% fat	1/2 cup	2	100
Honeynut Cheerios	1 cup	1	135	creamed	1/2 cup	5	120
Kashi	1 cup	1	120	Cream Cheese			
Kix	1 cup	0	75	Kraft-free	2 T	0	25
Life	1 cup	0	160	"lite" Neufchatel	2 T	0	75
Nut'n Honey	1 cup	2	165	regular	1 oz.	10	100
Nutri-Grain	1 cup	1	135	Weight Watchers	1 oz.	2	35
Oat bran, cooked	1 cup	2	110	Edam	1 oz.	8	100
Oats, instant	1 packet	2	110	Feta	1 oz.	6	75
Peanut Butter Puffs, Reese's	1 cup	4	175	Gouda	1 oz.	8	100
Product 19	1 cup	0	110	Healthy Choice (chunk)	1 oz.	0	40
Puffed Rice	1 cup	0	60	Hot Pepper	1 oz.	7	90
Puffed Wheat	1 cup	0	45	Jarlsberg	1 oz.	7	100
Raisin Bran	1 cup	1	155	Kraft American Singles	1 oz.	7	90
Raisin Squares	1 cup	1	240	Kraft Free	1 oz.	0	45
Rice Chex	1 cup	0	110	Kraft Light'n Lively	1 oz.	4	70
Rice Krispies	1 cup	0	110	Limburger	1 oz.	8	95
Shredded Wheat	1 cup	0	85	Monterey Jack	1 oz.	9	110
Shredded Wheat Sqs, frt-fld,	1 cup	0	180	Mozzarella			
Special K	1 cup	0	110	part skim	1 oz.	5	75
Sugar Frosted Flakes	1 cup	0	150	whole milk	1 oz.	6	80
Sugar Smacks	1 cup	1	130	whole milk, low moisture	1 oz.	7	90
Team	1 cup	1	110	Muenster	1 oz.	9	105
Wheat Chex	1 cup	1	170	Parmesan			
Wheaties	1 cup	1	100	grated	1 T	2	25
Cheese				hard	1 oz.	7	110
Alpine Lace, Free'n Lean				Port wine, cold pack	1 oz.	9	100
American	1 oz.	0	35	Provolone	1 oz.	8	100
Cheddar	1 oz.	0	35	Ricotta			
Mozzarella	1 oz.	0	35	"lite" reduced fat	1/2 cup	4	110
American				part skim	1/2 cup	10	170
light	1 oz.	4	70	whole milk	1/2 cup	16	215
processed	1 oz.	9	105	Romano	1 oz.	8	110
Blue	1 oz.	8	100	Roquefort	1 oz.	9	105
Brick	1 oz.	8	105	Smoked cheese product	1 oz.	7	90
Brie	1 oz.	8	95	Swiss			
Caraway	1 oz.	8	110	Aged	1 oz.	8	110
Cheddar	1 oz.	9	115	Processed	1 oz.	7	95
				Velveeta Light	1 oz.	4	70

Nutritional Information

Food Item	Amount	Fat Gm.	Calories
Desserts & Toppings			
Apple Betty, fruit crisps	1/2 cup	13	340
Baklava	1 piece	29	425
Brownie			
chocolate, plain	1 small	3	160
choc.w/ walnuts & icing	1 medium	5	180
Hostess	1 small	6	150
Little Debbie, chocolate	1 small	4	110
Pepperidge Farm	1	9	170
Snackwell brownie	1	2	130
Cake			
angel food	1/12 cake	0	160
banana w/ frosting	1/12 cake	16	390
black forest	1/12 cake	14	280
butter w/ frosting	1/12 cake	13	380
carrot w/ frosting	1/12 cake	19	420
chocolate w/ frosting	1/12 cake	17	390
chocolate,			
Betty Crocker lite	1/10 cake	3	230
coconut w/ frosting	1/12 cake	18	395
German chocolate			
w/ frosting	1/12 cake	18	400
gingerbread	2 1/2" slice	3	270
lemon chiffon	1/12 cake	4	190
lemon w/ frosting	1/12 cake	13	360
marble w/ frosting	1/12 cake	16	410
pineapple upside-down	2 1/2" slice	9	240
pound	1/12 cake	9	200
pnd, Entenmann fat-free	1 oz. slice	0	70
shortbread w/ fruit	1 piece	9	345
spice w/ frosting	1/12 cake	11	325
sponge	1 piece	3	195
Sweet Rewards	1/8 cake	0	170
white w/ frosting	1/12 cake	14	370
yellow w/ frosting	1/12 cake	16	390
Cheesecake	1/8 pie	22	370
Cobbler			
w/ biscuit topping	1/2 cup	6	210
w/ pie crust topping	1/2 cup	9	235
Cookies			
animal crackers	15 cookies	3	120
Bordeaux, Pepperidge Farm	1	2	40
Capri, Pepperidge Farm	1	5	80
Chips Ahoy, reduced fat	3	6	150
Chips Deluxe, Keebler,			
red. fat	1	3	70
chocolate	1	3	55
chocolate chip, homemade	1	4	70
choc chip, Pepperidge Farm	1 large	7	160
fig bar	1	1	55
fudge cookie cakes, Snackwell	1	0	50
gingersnap	1	2	35
graham cracker,			
chocolate cvrd.	1	3	60
lemon Nut, Pepperidge Farm	1 large	9	170
macaroon, coconut	1	2	50
Milano, Pepperidge Farm	1	4	60
molasses	1	2	70
oatmeal	1	3	80
oatmeal, raisin	1	3	80
oatmeal Pepperidge Farm	1	6	155
Oreo	1	2	50
reduced fat	3	5	140
Orleans, Pepperidge Farm	1	2	30
peanut butter	1	3	70
Rice Krispie bar	1	2	90
shortbread	1	2	40
Snackwell cream sandwich	1	1	55
sugar	1	3	90
sugar wafers	2 small	2	55
tea biscuit	1	1	20
Teddy Grahams, Nabisco	25	4	140
Vanilla crm sandwich, reg	1	3	70
Vanilla crm sndw, Snackwell's	3	4	165
Vanilla Wafers	3	2	50
Vienna Finger, Sunshine, red.	3	5	195
Cream Puff	1	15	245
Creamsicle	1 bar	3	105
Cupcake			
chocolate w/ icing	1	5	160
yellow w/ icing	1	6	160
Custard, baked	1/2 cup	7	150
Date bar	1 bar	3	95
Dreamsicle	1 bar	6	205
Dumpling, fruit	1 piece	15	325
Eclair			
w/ chocolate icing & custard	1 small	15	315
w/ chocolate icing & whipped	1 small	26	295
Frosting			
chocolate	3 T	5	150
cream cheese	3 T	7	170
lemon	3 T	4	140

Nutritional Information

Food Item	Amount	Fat Gm.	Calories	Food Item	Amount	Fat Gm.	Calories
Desserts and Toppings (continued)				blueberry	1/8 pie	17	385
ready-to-spread	1/2 tube	7	170	Boston cream pie	1/8 pie	8	260
seven-minute	3 T	0	135	cherry	1/8 pie	18	420
vanilla	3 T	4	140	chocolate cream	1/8 pie	13	310
Fruitcake	2 oz.	6	155	chocolate meringue	1/8 pie	18	380
Fudgesicle	1 bar	0	195	coconut cream or custard	1/8 pie	19	365
Gelatin				key lime	1/8 pie	19	390
low cal.	1/2 cup	0	10	lemon chiffon	1/8 pie	13	335
regular	1/2 cup	0	70	lemon meringue	1/8 pie	12	320
Granola bar	1 bar	6	140	mincemeat	1/8 pie	18	435
Hostess products				peach	1/8 pie	17	420
Cupcake	1	7	205	pecan	1/8 pie	23	510
Ding Dong	1	9	170	pumpkin	1/8 pie	17	365
Fruit Snack Pie	1	20	400	raisin	1/8 pie	13	325
Ho Ho	1	7	135	rhubarb	1/8 pie	17	405
Honey Bun	1	33	570	strawberry	1/8 pie	9	230
Snoball	1	4	150	sweet potato	1/8 pie	18	340
Twinkie	1	4	145	Pie tart, fruit filled	1 pie	19	360
Ice cream bar				Popsicle			
chocolate coated	1 bar	11	180	Kemps sugar-free	1	0	5
toffee crunch	1 bar	10	150	regular	1	0	95
Ice cream cake roll	1 slice	7	160	Pudding			
Ice cream cone (cone only)	1 medium	0	45	most flavors	1/2 cup	5	170
Ice cream drumstick	1	10	190	bread	1/2 cup	8	220
Ice cream sandwich	1	6	170	chocolate w/ whole milk	1/2 cup	9	245
Ice cream				pistachio, sugar-free w/skim	1/2 cup	0	70
chocolate	1/2 cup	7	135	rice	1/2 cup	6	180
chocolate gourmet	1/2 cup	12	175	tapioca	1/2 cup	5	125
fat-free	1/2 cup	0	110	Pudding Pop, frozen	1	2	75
French vanilla soft serve	1/2 cup	11	185	Sherbet	1/2 cup	2	135
light vanilla	1/2 cup	4	140	Souffle, chocolate	1/2 cup	4	65
strawberry	1/2 cup	6	130	Strudel, fruit	1/2 cup	1	50
vanilla	1/2 cup	7	135	Toppings			
vanilla, Haagen-Dazs	1/2 cup	17	250	butterscotch, caramel	3 T	0	155
Weight Watchers (1 % fat)	1/2 cup	9	80	chocolate fudge	2 T	4	100
Ice Milk				chocolate syrup, Hershey	2 T	0	70
chocolate	1/2 cup	3	90	marshmallow creme	3 T	0	160
soft serve, all flavors	1/2 cup	2	110	milk chocolate fudge	2 T	5	120
strawberry	1/2 cup	2	105	Mrs. Richardson's			
vanilla	1/2 cup	3	90	butterscotch	2 T	1	130
Ladyfinger	1	2	80	caramel, fat-free	2 T	0	130
Lemon bars	1 bar	3	70	hot fudge, fat-free	2 T	0	110
Mousse, chocolate	1/2 cup	15	190	pineapple	3 T	0	145
Napoleon	1 avg. pc.	15	285	strawberry	3 T	0	140
Pie				whipped topping			
apple	1/8 pie	17	350	aerosol	1/4 cup	4	45
banana cream or custard	1/8 pie	14	355	frozen	1/4 cup	4	80

Nutritional Information

Food Item	Amount	Fat Gm.	Calories	Food Item	Amount	Fat Gm.	Calories
Desserts and Toppings (continued)				Lobster, northern			
non-dairy lite	¼ cup	2	30	boiled	3 oz.	2	80
whipping cream				broiled w/ fat	12 oz.	24	310
heavy, fluid	1 T	6	50	Mackerel			
light, fluid	1 T	5	45	Atlantic	3 oz.	12	190
Turnover, fruit filled	1	19	225	Mussels			
Yogurt, frozen				canned	3 oz.	3	100
Low fat	1/2 cup	3	110	raw	3 oz.	2	75
Non fat	1/2 cup	0	80	Ocean perch			
Eggs				baked	3 oz.	2	100
Boiled/poached	1	6	80	fried	3 oz.	10	185
Fried w. 1/2 T fat	1	10	110	Octopus	3 oz.	1	70
Omelet				Oysters			
plain, 3 egg	1	21	270	canned	3 oz.	2	60
Denver, 3 egg	1	26	300	fried	3 oz.	10	170
Scrambled with milk	1	8	100	raw	6 medium	2	60
Substitute, Egg Beaters	¼ cup	0	30	Perch	3 oz.	1	80
Egg White	1	0	15	Pike			
Egg Yolk	1	6	65	northern	3 oz.	1	80
Fish (all baked w/o added fat)				walleye	3 oz.	1	80
Anchovy, canned	3 fillets	1	20	Pollock	3 oz.	1	80
Bass, cooked	3 oz.	4	125	Red snapper	3 oz.	2	80
Catfish	3 oz.	3	90	Roughy, orange	3 oz.	6	110
Caviar	1 Tbsp.	2	40	Salmon			
Clams				baked/broiled	3 oz.	6	150
canned, solids only	3 oz.	2	125	pink, canned	3 oz.	5	105
meat only	5 large	1	80	smoked	3 oz.	8	150
soft, raw	4 large	2	60	Sardines	3 oz.	8	135
Cod	3 oz.	1	90	Scallops			
Crab				cooked	3 oz.	1	70
Alaskan King	3 oz.	1	85	fried	3 oz.	9	170
cake	3 oz.	9	155	Sea bass	3 oz.	1	80
Crappie	3 oz.	1	70	Shrimp			
Flounder	3 oz.	0	60	fried	3 oz.	10	200
Fishstick, breaded	3 oz.	3	75	raw	3 oz.	1	90
Gefilte	3 oz.	2	70	Sole	3 oz.	0	60
Grouper	3 oz.	1	75	Squid			
Haddock				fried	3 oz.	6	150
baked	3 oz.	1	70	raw	3 oz.	1	110
Halibut	3 oz.	2	90	Sushi	3 oz.	4	120
Herring				Swordfish	3 oz.	4	100
canned or smoked	3 oz.	11	180	Trout			
pickled	3 oz.	15	235	brook	3 oz.	2	85
Lake trout	3 oz.	17	200	rainbow	3 oz.	9	165
				Tuna			
				light, canned in oil	3 oz.	20	230
				canned in water	3 oz.	1	100

Nutritional Information

Food Item	Amount	Fat Gm.	Calories
Fish (continued)			
White, canned in water	3 oz.	1	100
Yellowfin raw	3 oz.	1	90
Fruit			
Apple			
dried	1/2 cup	0	155
fresh	1 medium	0	80
Applesauce, unsweetened	1/2 cup	0	50
Apricots			
dried	5 halves	0	80
fresh	3 medium	0	50
Avocado	1	29	325
Banana	1 medium	1	105
Blackberries			
fresh	1 cup	0	75
frozen, unsweetened	1 cup	1	100
Blueberries			
fresh	1 cup	1	80
frozen, unsweetened	1 cup	1	80
Boysenberries, frzn, unswtned	1 cup	0	65
Cantaloupe	1 cup	0	60
Cherries			
fresh	1/2 cup	1	50
maraschino	1/4 cup	0	55
sour, canned in heavy syrup	1/2 cup	0	115
Cranberries, fresh	1 cup	0	45
Cranberry sauce	1/2 cup	0	210
Cranberry-orange relish	1/2 cup	1	245
Craisins	1/4 cup	0	100
Dates, whole, dried	1/2 cup	0	230
Figs			
canned	3 figs	0	75
dried, uncooked	10 figs	1	475
fresh	1 medium	0	40
Fruit cocktail, canned w/ juice	1 cup	0	110
Fruit Roll-Up	1	1	50
Fruit Snacks	1 svg.	0	80
Grapes, Thompson seedless	1/2 cup	0	95
Grapefruit	1/2 medium	0	40
Guava	1 medium	0	45
Honeydew melon	1/4 small	0	30
Kiwi	1 medium	0	50
Kumquat	1 medium	0	10
Lemon	1 medium	0	20
Lime	1 medium	0	20
Mandarin oranges, canned	1/2 cup	0	50
Mango	1 medium	1	135
Melon balls,	1 cup	0	55
Mixed fruit, dried	1/2 cup	1	250
Mixed fruit, frozen, unswtned	1 cup	1	245
Nectarine	1 medium	1	70
Orange	1 medium	0	60
Papaya	1 medium	0	120
Peach			
canned in heavy syrup	1 cup	0	190
canned in light syrup	1 cup	0	135
canned, water pack	1 cup	0	60
fresh	1 medium	0	40
Pear			
canned in heavy syrup	1 cup	0	190
canned in light syrup	1 cup	0	145
fresh	1 medium	1	100
Persimmon	1 medium	0	30
Pineapple			
canned in syrup	1 cup	2	190
canned, unsweetened	1 cup	0	140
fresh	1 cup	1	80
Plum			
canned in heavy syrup	1/2 cup	0	120
fresh	1 medium	1	35
Pomegranate	1 medium	0	100
Prunes, dried, cooked	1/2 cup	0	110
Raisins	1/4 cup	0	100
Raspberries			
fresh	1 cup	0	60
frozen, sweetened	1 cup	0	105
Rhubarb	1 cup	0	25
Strawberries			
fresh	1 cup	0	45
frozen, sweetened	1 cup	0	245
frozen, unsweetened	1 cup	0	50
Tangerine	1 medium	0	35
Watermelon	1 cup	0	50
Fruit/Veg. Juices			
Apple cider	1 cup	0	120
Apple juice	1 cup	0	115
Apricot juice	1 cup	0	125
Carrot juice	1 cup	0	80
Cranberry juice cocktail			
low cal	1 cup	0	45
regular	1 cup	0	150
Cranberry-apple juice	1 cup	0	130

Nutritional Information

Food Item	Amount	Fat Gm.	Calories
Fruit/Veg. Juices (continued)			
Grape juice	1 cup	0	155
Grapefruit juice	1 cup	0	95
Hawaiian Punch, regular	6 oz.	0	90
Hi-C	6 oz.	0	95
Lemon juice	2 T	0	10
Lime juice	2 T	0	10
Orange juice	1 cup	0	110
Orange-grapefruit juice	1 cup	0	110
Peach nectar	1 cup	0	135
Pear nectar	1 cup	0	150
Pineapple juice	1 cup	0	140
Pineapple-orange juice	1 cup	0	125
Prune juice	1 cup	0	180
Raspberry juice	1 cup	0	120
Tomato juice	1 cup	0	40
V-8 juice	1 cup	0	50
Gravies, Sauces, & Dips			
Au Jus, mix	1 cup	0	50
Barbecue sauce	1 T	0	10
Bearnaise sauce, mix	1/4 pkg.	25	265
Brown Gravy			
beef, Heinz fat-free	1/4 cup	0	15
canned	1/2 cup	3	80
from mix	1/2 cup	0	30
homemade	1/4 cup	14	165
Catsup	1 T	0	15
Chicken Gravy			
canned	1/2 cup	8	120
from mix	1/2 cup	1	40
giblet from can	1/4 cup	2	35
Pepperidge Farm, 98% fat-free	1/4 cup	1	25
Chip Dip, Light	2 T	2	35
Chili sauce	1 T	0	15
Cocktail sauce	2 T	0	25
Dip, sour cream-based	2 T	5	50
Guacamole dip	1 oz.	12	110
Hollandaise sauce	1/4 cup	18	180
Horseradish sauce, Kraft	1 T	2	20
Home-style gravy, mix	1/4 cup	1	25
Mushroom gravy			
canned	1/2 cup	4	75
from mix	1/2 cup	1	35
Mushroom sauce, from Mix	1/4 pkg.	3	70
Mustard			
brown	1 T	1	15
yellow	1 T	1	10

Food Item	Amount	Fat Gm.	Calories
Onion dip	2 T	4	60
Onion gravy, mix	1/2 cup	1	40
Pesto sauce, commercial	1 oz.	15	155
Picante sauce	6 T	1	50
Pork gravy mix	1/2 cup	1	40
Sour cream sauce	1/4 cup	12	125
Soy sauce	1 T	0	10
Soy sauce, reduced sodium	1 T	0	10
Spaghetti sauce			
canned, w/o meat	1/2 cup	4	80
Healthy Choice, extra chunky	1/2 cup	5	50
homemade w/ meat	1/2 cup	18	240
Pasta Toss, Ragu	1/2 cup	8	120
Prego w/ mushrooms	1/2 cup	6	135
Prego w/ meat flavor	1/2 cup	6	140
Ragu, extra chunky	1/2 cup	6	120
Ranch dip	1 T	1	30
Spinach dip	2 T	7	75
Steak sauce	1 T	0	10
Stir fry sauce	1 T	1	30
Stroganoff sauce, mix	1/4 pkg.	3	75
Sweet & sour sauce	1/4 pkg.	0	130
Tabasco sauce	1 T	0	6
Taco sauce	1 T	0	7
Tartar sauce	1 T	8	70
fat-free	1 T	0	25
Teriyaki sauce	1 T	0	15
Turkey gravy			
canned	1/2 cup	3	75
mix	1/2 cup	1	40
White sauce	1/2 cup	12	220
Worcestershire sauce	1 T	0	10
Meats (all cooked w/o fat, unless noted)			
Beef (extra lean, 7.5-12.4% fat)	3 oz.	8	170
arm/blade pot roast	3 oz.	8	170
club steak, lean	3 oz.	11	205
flank steak, fat trimmed	3 oz.	7	165
hindshank, lean	3 oz.	8	180
liver			
braised	3 oz.	4	135
fried	3 oz.	7	185
porterhouse steak, lean	3 oz.	9	200
rib steak, lean	3 oz.	8	180
round			
bottom, lean	3 oz.	8	180
eye of round, lean	3 oz.	4	110

Nutritional Information

Food Item	Amount	Fat Gm.	Calories	Food Item	Amount	Fat Gm.	Calories
Meats (continued)				loin chop			
rump, lean, pot roasted	3 oz.	6	155	lean	3 oz.	7	155
top, lean	3 oz.	5	180	lean and fat	3 oz.	18	260
sirloin steak, lean	3 oz.	8	170	rib chop			
sirloin steak, lean & fat	3 oz.	16	240	lean	3 oz.	7	155
sirloin tip, lean, roasted	3 oz.	8	175	lean and fat	3 oz.	18	250
tenderloin, lean, broiled	3 oz.	10	190	shoulder			
top sirloin, lean, broiled	3 oz.	7	170	lean	3 oz.	9	215
Beef, extra lean, 15% fat	3 oz.	13	225	lean and fat	3 oz.	23	370
chuck, separable lean	3 oz.	13	225	Miscellaneous meats			
cubed steak	3 oz.	13	225	bacon substitute, strip	2 strips	4	50
hamburger				beefalo	3 oz.	5	160
extra lean	3 oz.	12	215	frog legs			
rinsed and drained	3 oz.	7	190	cooked	4 large	1	70
rib roast, lean	3 oz.	7	190	flour-coated and fried	6 large	29	420
sirloin tips, roasted	3 oz.	13	225	rabbit, stewed	3 oz.	9	185
stew meat, round, raw	3 oz.	12	225	tongue	1 oz.	6	75
T-bone, lean only	3 oz.	9	200	venison, roasted	3 oz.	2	135
tenderloin , marbled	3 oz.	13	225	Pork			
Beef, lean, approx. 20% fat	3 oz.	17	245	bacon			
chuck, ground	3 oz.	20	285	cured, broiled	1 slice	3	35
hamburger, regular	3 oz.	17	245	cured, raw	1 slice	16	155
meatballs	3 oz.	15	210	bacon bits	1 T	1	20
porterhouse steak, marbled	3 oz.	17	245	blade			
rib steak	3 oz.	13	245	lean	3 oz.	9	190
rump, pot roast	3 oz.	17	245	lean and fat	3 oz.	15	250
short ribs, lean only	3 oz.	17	245	butt			
sirloin, broiled	3 oz.	16	245	lean	3 oz.	12	260
Beef, regular, approx. 25% fat	3 oz.	23	305	lean and fat	3 oz.	24	295
arm/blade, pot roast	3 oz.	23	305	Canadian bacon, broiled	1 oz.	2	40
brisket, lean and marbled	3 oz.	26	315	Ham			
chuck, stew meat	3 oz.	30	365	cured, butt, lean	3 oz.	4	140
corned, medium fat	3 oz.	26	315	cured, butt, lean and fat	3 oz.	11	210
rib roast	3 oz.	26	315	cured, canned	3 oz.	5	120
ribeye steak, marbled	3 oz.	33	380	cured, shank, lean	3 oz.	5	150
short ribs	3 oz.	27	320	cured, shank, lean and fat	2 slices	14	255
sirloin, ground	3 oz.	23	305	fresh, lean	3 oz.	5	190
steak, chicken fried	3 oz.	26	320	fresh, lean and fat	3 oz.	15	265
T-bone , broiled	3 oz.	23	305	ham loaf, glazed	3 oz.	13	210
Lamb				loin chop			
blade chop,				lean	3 oz.	7	170
lean	3 oz.	6	128	lean and fat	3 oz.	14	295
lean and fat	3 oz.	22	325	smoked	3 oz.	9	150
leg				smoked, 95% lean	3 oz.	5	125
lean	3 oz.	7	155	picnic			
lean and fat	3 oz.	12	220	cured, lean	3 oz.	9	180
				fresh, lean	3 oz.	6	130
				shoulder, lean	2 slices	5	160

Nutritional Information

Food Item	Amount	Fat Gm.	Calories
Meats (continued)			
shoulder, marbled	2 slices	14	235
pig's feet, pickled	1 oz.	4	55
rib chop, trimmed	3 oz.	9	180
rib roast, trimmed	3 oz.	9	175
sausage			
brown and serve	1 oz.	9	105
link	1/2 oz.	5	50
patty	1 oz.	8	100
sirloin, lean, roasted	3 oz.	9	175
spareribs, roasted	6 medium	35	395
tenderloin, lean, roast	3 oz.	4	135
Top loin chop, trimmed	3 oz.	7	165
Processed meats			
bacon substitute	2 strips	4	50
beef breakfast strips	2 strips	7	115
beef jerky	1 oz.	4	110
beef, chipped	2 slices	3	115
bologna, beef and pork	1 oz.	8	85
bratwurst			
pork	3 oz. link	33	380
pork and beef	3 oz. link	29	340
turkey	3 oz. link	10	160
braunschweiger	1 oz.	8	65
corn dog	1	20	330
corned beef	3 oz.	9	95
ham, chopped	1 oz.	2	55
ham, Louis Rich Carving Bd	3 slices	2	75
hot dog			
beef or pork	1	13	145
chicken	1	9	115
Healthy Choice	2	3	100
Hormel 97% fat-free	1	1	45
turkey	1	8	100
kielbasa (Polish sausage)	1 oz.	8	80
knockwurst, knackwurst	2 oz. link	19	210
liver paté, goose	1 oz.	12	130
Lunchables			
ham & cheddar	1 pkg.	22	360
low fat ham & swiss combo	1 pkg.	10	360
pepperoni	1 oz.	13	150
pork and beef	1 oz.	9	100
salami			
cooked	1 oz.	10	115
dry/hard	1 oz.	10	125
sausage			
Italian, mild or hot	2 oz. link	17	215

Food Item	Amount	Fat Gm.	Calories
Polish	1 oz. link	8	90
smoked	2 oz. link	20	230
Vienna	1 sausage	4	45
Spam	1 oz.	7	90
turkey ham	3 oz.	3	105
Veal			
arm steak			
lean	3 oz.	4	150
lean and fat	3 oz.	16	255
blade			
lean	3 oz.	7	200
lean and fat	3 oz.	14	240
cutlet			
breaded	3 oz.	13	270
round, lean	3 oz.	11	170
round, lean and fat	3 oz.	13	240
loin, medium fat, broiled	3 oz.	11	200
loin chop			
lean	3 oz.	5	150
lean and fat	3 oz.	11	215
rib chop			
lean	3 oz.	7	125
lean and fat	3 oz.	18	265
rump, marbled, roasted	3 oz.	9	195
sirloin			
lean roasted	3 oz.	3	150
marbled, roasted	3 oz.	6	155
sirloin steak, ground	3 oz.	14	230
sirloin steak			
lean	3 oz.	5	175
lean and fat	3 oz.	17	260
Milk & Dairy Products			
Buttermilk			
1% fat	1 cup	2	100
dry	1 T	0	25
Chocolate milk			
2% fat	1 cup	5	180
whole	1 cup	8	250
Condensed milk			
sweet	1/2 cup	14	440
sweet, fat-free	1/2 cup	0	440
Creamer, non dairy Intl. vanilla	2 T	3	80
Evaporated			
skim	1/2 cup	0	100
whole	1/2 cup	10	125
Half and half, fat-free	2 T	0	20

Nutritional Information

Food Item	Amount	Fat Gm.	Calories
Milk and Dairy Products (continued)			
Malted milk	1 cup	10	240
Milk			
non-fat dry powder	1/4 cup	0	110
skim fat	1 cup	0	90
1% fat	1 cup	3	100
2% fat	1 cup	5	120
Whole milk, 3.5% fat	1 cup	8	150
dry powder	1/4 cup	9	160
Milk shake			
chocolate	1 cup	17	340
soft serve	1 cup	7	220
vanilla	1 cup	15	270
Ovaltine w/1 % milk	1 cup	3	170
Yogurt			
Dannon Lt/Crunchy			
car. apple	8 oz.	0	150
frozen, low fat	1/2 cup	3	115
frozen, non-fat	1/2 cup	0	80
fruit flavored, low fat	1 cup	3	225
fruit flavored, non-fat	1 cup	0	160
low fat	1 cup	3	145
plain	1 cup	8	190
skim, non-fat	1 cup	0	130
vanilla, low fat	1 cup	3	190
whole milk	1 cup	7	140
Yoplait Vanilla'N Wafer	7 oz.	2	220
Miscellaneous			
Bac-Os	11	1	30
Bouillon cube, beef or chicken	1	0	10
Chewing gum	1 stick	0	10
Gelatin	1/2 cup	0	80
Honey	1 T	0	65
Horseradish	1 T	1	12
Icing, decorator	1 T	2	70
Icing, all varieties	1 T	1	55
Jelly, all varieties	1 T	0	50
Marmalade, citrus	1 T	0	50
Meat tenderizer	1 tsp.	0	0
Molasses	1 T	0	50
Olives			
black	2 large	4	40
Greek	3 medium	7	70
green	2 medium	2	15
Peanut butter			
regular	1 T	9	150
Skippy reduced fat	1 T	6	95

Food Item	Amount	Fat Gm.	Calories
Pickle relish	1 T	0	20
Pickles			
bread & butter	4 slices	0	20
dill	1 large	0	10
Kosher	1 oz.	0	10
sweet	1 oz.	0	145
Salt	1 tsp.	0	0
Shake'n Bake, General Foods	1/4 pkg.	3	70
Smoothies (Jamba Juice)			
Kiwi Berry Burner	24 oz.	0	420
Orange-A-Peel	24 oz.	1	420
Strawberry Wild	24 oz.	1	440
Aloha Pineapple	24 oz.	2	440
Jamba PowerBoost	24 oz.	2	450
Mango-A-Go-Go	24 oz.	2	460
Banana Berry	24 oz.	2	470
Spices and herbs	1 tsp.	0	5
Sugar substitutes	1 packet	0	5
Sugar, cane or beet	1 T	0	45
Syrup, all varieties	1 T	0	60
Mixed Dishes			
Baked beans w/ pork	1 cup	4	270
Beans & franks, canned	1 cup	16	365
Beans , refried			
canned	1 cup	3	270
refried w/ fat	1 cup	26	540
refried, fat-free	1 cup	0	250
Beef & vegetable stew	1 cup	10	220
Beef burgundy	1 cup	21	330
Beef noodle casserole	1 cup	20	330
Beef Oriental, Lean Cuisine	1 serving	9	270
Beef pie, frozen	8 oz.	23	430
Beef stew	1 cup	8	180
Beef stew, homemade	1 cup	14	225
Beef teriyaki, Stouffer's	1 serving	11	365
Beef,			
chipped, creamed, homemade	1 cup	22	350
chipped, creamed, frozen	5 1/2 oz.	16	235
short ribs w/ gravy, frozen	6 oz.	28	380
sloppy joe	6 oz.	14	230
Burrito			
bean w/ cheese	1 large	10	230
bean w/o cheese	1 large	3	140
beef	1 large	25	425
with guacamole, frozen	6 oz.	16	350
Cabbage roll w/ beef & rice	1 average	8	170

Nutritional Information

Food Item	Amount	Fat Gm.	Calories	Food Item	Amount	Fat Gm.	Calories
Mixed Dishes (continued)				Fajita, beef	1	18	400
Cannelloni, meat & cheese	1 piece	30	420	Fajita, chicken	1	12	365
Cheese soufflé	1 cup	11	175	Fettuccine Alfredo	1 cup	30	460
Chicken				Fillet of fish divan, frozen	8 oz.	2	180
á la king				Fish creole	1 cup	5	170
Stouffer's	1 serving	11	330	Fritter, corn	1 average	8	130
Swanson's	1 serving	12	180	Frozen dinners			
glazed, Lean Cuisine	1 serving	7	270	chipped steak	18 oz.	40	730
Chicken & dumplings	sm. serving	10	330	chopped beefsteak	11 oz.	26	440
Chicken & noodles, Stouffer's	1 serving	15	250	fried chicken	11 oz.	28	560
Chicken & rice casserole	1 cup	18	365	meat loaf	11 oz.	16	360
Chicken & vegetable stir-fry	1 cup	7	140	Salisbury steak	11 oz.	29	500
Chicken Cacciatore, Stouffer's	1 serving	11	310	turkey	11 oz.	11	360
Chicken divan, Stouffer's	1 serving	22	335	Green pepper stfd. w/ rice, beef	1 average	13	260
Chicken-fried steak	4 oz.	25	400	Ham salad w/ mayo	4 oz.	20	280
Chicken noodle casserole	1 cup	11	300	Ham spread, Spreadables	1/2 cup	19	205
Chicken pie				Hamburger Helper, all types	8 oz.	19	375
frozen	8 oz.	23	400	Hamburger rice casserole	8 oz.	21	370
homemade	8 oz.	32	550	Hot Pockets, ham and cheese	1	12	360
Chicken salad, regular	4 oz.	21	280	Lasagna			
Chili				cheese, frozen	8 oz.	11	320
w/ beans	1 cup	15	300	homemade	1 serving	21	420
w/o beans	1 cup	20	300	zucchini, Lean Cuisine	11 oz.	6	260
Chop suey				Lo mein, Chinese	1 cup	7	185
beef	1 cup	17	300	Lobster			
chicken	1 cup	7	125	Cantonese	1 cup	20	335
Chow mein				Newburg	8 oz.	24	440
beef, canned, La Choy	1 cup	2	70	salad	1/2 cup	7	120
chicken, canned, La Choy	1 cup	2	70	Macaroni & cheese			
homemade	1 cup	9	220	box mix	1 cup	18	385
noodles	1 cup	14	260	Kraft Thick'n Creamy	2/3 cup	5	510
Corned-beef hash	1 cup	23	375	Macaroni & cheese, frozen	6 oz.	12	260
Creamed chipped beef	1 cup	22	350	Manicotti, cheese & tomato	1 piece	11	240
Deviled crab	1/2 cup	15	230	Meat loaf, w/ reg. ground beef	3 oz.	18	280
Deviled eggs	1/2 egg	5	70	Onion rings	10 avg.	17	230
Egg foo yung w/ sauce	1 piece	11	130	Oysters Rockefeller	6-8 oysters	14	230
Egg salad	1/2 cup	17	210	Pizza			
Eggplant Parmesan	1 cup	24	350	cheese	1 slice	10	180
Egg roll				cheese, French bread	5 1/8 oz.	13	330
chicken, Chun King	1 average	7	210	combination w/ meat	1 slice	17	270
homemade	1 average	10	150	deep dish, cheese	1 slice	13	420
pork, Chun King	1 average	8	220	pepperoni, frozen	1 slice	18	360
Enchilada				Pizza rolls, Jeno's	3 pieces	7	130
bean, beef, & cheese	1	14	250	Pork, sweet & sour	1 1/2 cup	22	390
beef, frozen	8 oz.	17	260	Quiche			
cheese, frozen	8 oz.	21	360	Lorraine (bacon)	1 slice	20	360
chicken, frozen	12 oz.	12	270	plain or vegetable	1 slice	17	310

Nutritional Information

Food Item	Amount	Fat Gm.	Calories	Food Item	Amount	Fat Gm.	Calories
Mixed Dishes (continued)				**Nuts & Seeds**			
Ratatouille	1/2 cup	7	90	Almonds	12-15	9	105
Ravioli, canned	1 cup	7	240	Brazil nuts	4 medium	11	115
Ravioli w/ meat & tomato sauce	1 piece	3	50	Cashews, roasted	6-8	8	95
Salisbury steak w/ gravy	8 oz.	27	365	Chestnuts, fresh	3 small	1	65
Salmon patty, homemade	6 oz.	20	400	Coconut, dried, shredded	1/3 cup	9	135
Sandwiches				Hazelnuts (filberts)	10-12	11	105
BLT w/ mayo	1	16	280	Macadamia nuts, roasted	6 medium	12	120
chicken w/ mayo	1	14	300	Mixed nuts			
club house w/ mayo	1	20	590	dry roasted	1 oz.	14	160
corned beef on rye	1	11	290	w/ peanuts	1 oz.	15	150
egg salad	1	12	280	w/o peanuts	1 oz.	16	175
ham & mayo	1	10	280	Peanut butter			
peanut butter & jelly	1	10	370	creamy or chunky	1 T	8	90
Reuben	1	33	530	Skippy reduced fat	1 T	6	95
roast beef & gravy	1	25	430	Peanuts			
roast beef & mayo	1	22	430	chopped	2 T	9	100
sub w/ salami & cheese	1	41	780	honey roasted	2 T	9	110
tuna salad	1	14	280	in shell	1 cup	18	210
turkey, lettuce, & mayo	1	18	400	Pecans	2 T	9	90
turkey breast	1	5	285	Pine nuts (pignolia)	2 T	9	85
Shepherd's pie	12 oz.	24	400	Pistachios	2 T	8	90
Shrimp creole	1 cup	20	150	Sesame nut mix	2 T	5	65
Spaghetti				Sesame seeds	2 T	9	95
w/ meat sauce	1 cup	16	320	Soynuts	1/4 cup	5	75
w/ tomato sauce	1 cup	2	180	Sunflower seeds	2 T	9	100
SpaghettiOs, Franco American	1 cup	2	160	Trail mix w/ seeds, nuts			
Spinach souffle	1 cup	15	210	carob	2 T	5	85
Stroganoff, beef, Stouffer's	9 3/4 oz.	20	390	walnut	2 T	8	80
Sweet & sour pork	1 cup	22	380				
Taco beef	1 medium	17	270	**Pasta & Rice**			
Tortellini, meat or cheese	1 cup	15	360	Macaroni			
Tostada w/ refried beans	1 medium	16	290	semolina or durham	1 cup	1	160
Tuna Helper	1 cup	10	295	whole wheat	1 cup	1	180
Tuna noodle casserole	1 cup	13	315	Noodles			
Tuna salad				Alfredo	1 cup	30	460
oil pack w/ mayo	1/2 cup	16	220	almondine, from mix	1/4 pkg.	12	240
water pack w/ mayo	1/2 cup	10	170	cellophane, fried	1 cup	4	140
Veal Parmigiana				egg	1 cup	2	200
frozen	6 oz.	20	340	mostaccioli	1 cup	2	200
homemade	1 cup	25	485	ramen, all varieties	1 cup	6	190
scallopini	1 cup	20	420	rice	1 cup	0	140
Welsh rarebit	1 cup	30	415	Romanoff	1 cup	23	370
Won Ton w/ pork, fried	1 piece	4	80	Red beans and rice, Vigo	1/3 cup	0	190
Yorkshire pudding	1 serving	3	50				

Nutritional Information

Food Item	Amount	Fat Gm.	Calories
Pasta & Rice (continued)			
Rice			
brown	1/2 cup	1	115
fried	1/2 cup	7	180
long grain, wild	1/2 cup	2	120
pilaf	1/2 cup	7	170
Spanish style	1/2 cup	2	105
white	1/2 cup	1	110
Rice A Roni	1/2 cup	1	110
Spaghetti, enriched	1 cup	1	160
Poultry			
Chicken			
Breast			
w/ skin, fried	1/2 breast	10	235
w/o skin, fried	1/2 breast	6	180
w/ skin, roasted	1/2 breast	8	190
w/o skin, roasted	1/2 breast	3	140
Fryers			
w/ skin, batter dipped, fried	3 oz.	15	250
w/o skin, fried	3 oz.	9	205
w/ skin, roasted	3 oz.	12	205
w/o skin roasted	3 oz.	6	160
Leg			
w/ skin, fried	1 leg	8	120
w/ skin, roasted	1 leg	6	110
w/o skin roasted	1 leg	2	75
Roll, light meat	3 oz.	6	135
Thigh			
w/ skin, fried	1 thigh	12	180
w/ skin, roasted	1 thigh	10	150
w/o skin, roasted	1 thigh	6	110
Wing			
w/ skin, fried	1 wing	9	120
w/ skin, roasted	1 wing	7	100
w/o skin, roasted	1 wing	3	70
Duck			
w/ skin, roasted	3 oz.	24	290
w/o skin, roasted	3 oz.	10	175
Pheasant, raw breast	3 oz.	3	120
Turkey			
white meat,			
oven roasted	3 oz.	3	100
smoked	3 oz.	4	105
dark meat			
w/ skin, roasted	3 oz.	10	190
w/o skin, roasted	3 oz.	6	160

Food Item	Amount	Fat Gm.	Calories
ground, mixed meat	3 oz.	12	195
ground, all white meat	3 oz.	4	110
ham, cured	3 oz.	4	110
light meat			
w/ skin, roasted	3 oz.	7	170
w/o skin, roasted	3 oz.	3	135
loaf, breast meat	3 oz.	2	95
pastrami	1 oz.	1	40
patties, breaded, fried	1 patty	17	265
roll, light meat	3 oz.	6	125
salami	1 oz.	4	55
sausage, cooked	1 oz.	3	50
sliced w/ gravy, frozen	5 oz.	4	95
Salads			
Caesar salad w/o anchovies	1 cup	9	80
Carrot-raisin salad	1/2 cup	8	315
Chef salad w/o dressing	1 cup	8	110
Coleslaw			
w/ mayo-type dressing	1/2 cup	14	145
w/ vinaigrette	1/2 cup	5	75
Fruit salad			
fresh	1/2 cup	0	70
w/ mayo dressing	1/2 cup	8	220
Gelatin salad w/ fruit	1/2 cup	0	20
Macaroni salad w/ mayo	1/2 cup	13	200
Pasta primavera salad	1/2 cup	10	200
Potato salad	1 cup	20	360
German style	1/2 cup	3	140
w/ mayo dressing	1/2 cup	11	190
Seven-layer salad	1 cup	18	225
Taco salad w/ taco sauce	1 cup	14	200
Three-bean salad	1/2 cup	11	145
Three-bean salad, no oil	1/2 cup	0	90
Tuna salad, w/ mayo	1/2 cup	19	285
Waldorf salad w/ mayo	1/2 cup	25	310
Salad Dressings			
Balsamic Vinnegriette	2 T	9	70
Blue Cheese			
fat-free	1 oz.	0	20
regular	1 oz.	16	155
Buttermilk, from mix	1 oz.	12	120
Caesar	1 oz.	14	140
French			
creamy	1 oz.	14	140
reduced fat	1 oz.	2	40
regular	1 oz.	13	140

Nutritional Information

Food Item	Amount	Fat Gm.	Calories
Salad Dressings (continued)			
Green Goddess			
reduced fat	1 oz.	4	60
regular	1 oz.	14	140
Honey mustard	1 oz.	13	180
Italian			
creamy	1 oz.	9	100
reduced fat	1 oz.	3	30
regular zesty from mix	1 oz.	18	170
Kraft free	1 oz.	0	40
Kraft reduced calorie	1 oz.	2	50
Mayonnaise type			
reduced fat	1 oz.	4	40
regular	1 oz.	10	120
Oil & vinegar	1 oz.	15	140
Ranch			
w/ mayo	1 oz.	16	160
reduced fat	1 oz.	10	110
Russian			
reduced fat	1 oz.	1	45
regular	1 oz.	16	150
Sesame seed	1 oz.	14	140
Sweet & sour	1 oz.	2	60
Thousand Island			
reduced fat	1 oz.	3	50
regular	1 oz.	11	140
Western			
regular	2 T	13	130
lite	2 T	3	70
Snack Foods			
Bagel chips or crisps	1 oz.	9	150
Bugles	1 oz.	8	150
Bugles Lite	1 oz.	2	85
Cheese Puff Balls, Cheetos	1 oz.	11	160
Cheese Puffs, Cheetos	1 oz.	10	160
Cheese Balls, Planter's red. fat	30	3	70
Chex Mix, traditional	1 cup	5	195
Corn chips, Frito's			
lite	1 oz.	10	145
regular	1 oz.	10	155
Corn nuts, all flavors	1 oz.	4	120
Cracker Jacks	1 oz.	1	115
Doo-Dads, Nabisco	1/2 cup	6	140
Energy Bars (represents avg. for most flavors)			
Balance Bar, almond brownie	1	6	190
Clif bar, Chocolate Chip	1	4	240

Food Item	Amount	Fat Gm.	Calories
Luna, Chai tea	1	4	180
Power Bar, apple cinnamon	1	2	230
Tigers Milk Bar	1	5	140
Handisnacks, Cheez'n Pretzel	1 serving	6	110
Party mix (cereal, pretzels, nuts)	1 cup	23	310
Popcorn, air popped	1 cup	0	20
Popcorn			
Betty Crocker 94% fat-free	3 cups	1	55
caramel	1 cup	4	140
Cracker Jack, fat-free	1 cup	0	110
Healthy Choice	3 cups	1	60
microwave, plain	1 cup	3	50
microwave, w/ butter	1 cup	4	60
popped w/ oil	1 cup	2	40
Potato chips			
individually	10 chips	8	110
by weight	1 oz.	11	160
barbecue flavor	1 oz.	9	150
lite, Pringles	1 oz.	8	145
regular, Pringles	1 oz.	13	170
Potato Crisps, Frito Lay,			
baked	16	2	135
Potato sticks	1 oz.	10	150
Pretzels			
hard	1 oz.	1	110
soft	1 average	0	175
Rice cakes, Quaker caramel	1 cake	1	50
Tortilla chips			
baked w/o oil	1 oz.	1	100
Doritos	1 oz.	7	140
Tostitos	1 oz.	8	145
Soups			
Asparagus			
cream of, w/ milk	1 cup	8	160
cream of, w/ water	1 cup	4	90
Bean			
w/ bacon	1 cup	6	175
w/ franks	1 cup	7	190
w/ ham	1 cup	8	230
w/o meat	1 cup	3	140
Beef			
broth	1 cup	0	30
Chunky	1 cup	5	170
Beef barley	1 cup	1	70
Beef noodle	1 cup	3	85
Broccoli, creamy w/ water	1 cup	3	70

Nutritional Information

Food Item	Amount	Fat Gm.	Calories	Food Item	Amount	Fat Gm.	Calories
Soups (continued)				mushroom	1 cup	5	95
Campbell's Chunky				onion	1 pkg.	2	115
w/ meat	1 cup	5	170	tomato	1 cup	2	100
w/o meat	1 cup	4	120	vegetable beef	1 cup	1	50
Canned vegetable type				Gazpacho	1 cup	0	40
w/o meat	1 cup	2	70	Healthy Request			
Cheese w/ milk	1 cup	15	230	cream of mushroom	1 cup	3	70
Chicken				cream of chicken	1 cup	3	80
Chunky	1 cup	7	180	Homemade or restaurant style			
Cream of, w/ milk	1 cup	11	190	beer cheese	1 cup	23	310
Cream of, w/ water	1 cup	7	115	cauliflower, cream of, whl mlk	1 cup	10	165
Chicken and dumplings	1 cup	5	100	celery, cream of, whole milk	1 cup	11	165
Chicken/beef noodle or				chicken broth	1 cup	1	40
vegetable	1 cup	3	80	clam chowder			
Chicken gumbo	1 cup	1	55	Manhattan	1 cup	2	80
Chicken mushroom	1 cup	9	150	New England	1 cup	14	270
Chicken noodle				corn chowder	1 cup	12	250
Chunky	1 cup	6	115	fish chowder w/ whole milk	1 cup	13	285
w/ water	1 cup	2	75	gazipacho	1 cup	7	100
Chicken vegetable				mock turtle	1 cup	15	245
Chunky	1 cup	5	165	onion, French w/o cheese	1 cup	6	90
w/ water	1 cup	3	75	oyster stew w/ whole milk	1 cup	17	270
Chicken w/ noodles, Chunky	1 cup	5	180	seafood gumbo	1 cup	4	155
Chicken w/ rice				Lentil	1 cup	1	160
Chunky	1 cup	3	125	Minestrone			
w/ water	1 cup	2	60	Chunky	1 cup	3	130
Chicken wild rice	1 cup	2	75	w/ water	1 cup	2	80
Clam chowder				Mushroom, cream of			
Manhattan Chunky	1 cup	3	135	condensed	1 cup	23	310
New England	1 cup	7	160	w/ milk	1 cup	14	200
Consommé w/ gelatin	1 cup	0	30	w/ water	1 cup	9	130
Crab	1 cup	1	80	reduced fat	1 cup	7	140
Dehydrated soups				Onion	1 cup	2	60
asparagus, cream of	1 cup	2	60	Oyster stew w/ water	1 cup	4	60
bean w/ bacon	1 cup	3	105	Pea			
beef broth cube	1 cup	0	10	green, w/ water	1 cup	3	165
beef noodle	1 cup	1	40	split	1 cup	1	60
cauliflower	1 cup	2	70	split w/ ham	1 cup	4	190
chicken, cream of	1 cup	5	110	Potato, cream of, w/ milk	1 cup	7	160
chicken broth cube	1 cup	0	10	Shrimp, cream of, w/ milk	1 cup	9	165
chicken noodle	1 cup	1	50	Tomato			
chicken rice	1 cup	1	60	w/ milk	1 cup	6	160
clam chowder				w/ water	1 cup	2	100
Manhattan	1 cup	2	65	Tomato bisque w/ milk	1 cup	7	100
New England	1 cup	4	95	Tomato rice	1 cup	3	120
minestrone	1 cup	2	80	Turkey, Chunky	1 cup	4	135

Nutritional Information

Food Item	Amount	Fat Gm.	Calories
Soups (continued)			
Turkey noodle	1 cup	2	70
Turkey vegetable	1 cup	3	75
Vegetable, Chunky	1 cup	4	120
Vegetable w/ beef, Chunky	1 cup	3	135
Vegetable w/ beef, broth	1 cup	2	80
Vegetarian vegetable	1 cup	2	70
Won Ton	1 cup	2	90
Spreads, Oils & Creams			
Butter			
solid	1 T	12	110
whipped	1 T	9	90
Butter Buds, liquid	2 T	0	10
Cream			
light	1 T	3	30
medium (25% fat)	1 T	4	40
Cream substitute			
liquid/frozen	1/2 fl. oz.	1	20
powdered	1 T	1	10
Dijonnaise	1 T	3	30
Half & Half	1 T	2	20
Margarine			
liquid	1 T	11	100
solid (corn)	1 T	10	90
Mayonnaise			
low fat	1 T	1	25
regular	1 T	11	100
Miracle Whip	1 T	7	70
Mustard	1 T	1	10
No-stick spray, fat-free, (Pam)	1 spray	0	0
Oil			
canola	1 T	14	120
corn	1 T	14	120
olive	1 T	14	120
safflower	1 T	14	120
soybean	1 T	14	120
Sandwich spread, non-fat	1 T	0	25
Shortening, vegetable	1 T	12	105
Sour cream			
cultured	1 T	2	25
half & half, cultured	1 T	2	20
imitation	1 T	3	25
reduced calorie	1 T	1	15
fat-free	1 T	0	45
Tartar sauce	1 T	8	75

Food Item	Amount	Fat Gm.	Calories
Vegetables			
Alfalfa sprouts, raw	1 cup	0	5
Artichoke, boiled	1 medium	0	50
Artichoke hearts, boiled	1/2 cup	0	40
Asparagus, cooked	1/2 cup	0	20
Avocado	1 average	28	325
Bamboo shoots, raw	1/2 cup	0	20
Beans, baked			
all types cooked w/o fat	1/2 cup	0	125
baked, brown sugar & molasses	1/2 cup	1	130
baked, Bush's vegetarian	1/2 cup	0	130
baked w/ pork & tomato sauce	1/2 cup	2	190
baked, vegetarian	1/2 cup	1	160
home-style canned	1/2 cup	2	130
refried			
Old El Paso fat-free	1/2 cup	0	110
Ortega 98% fat-free	1/2 cup	3	140
Beets	1/2 cup	0	35
Black-eyed peas, cooked	1/2 cup	0	100
Broccoli			
cooked	1/2 cup	0	45
frozen in butter sauce	1/2 cup	2	50
frozen w/ cheese sauce	1/2 cup	6	115
frozen, chopped, cooked	1/2 cup	0	25
raw	1/2 cup	0	10
Brussels sprouts, cooked	1/2 cup	0	30
Butter beans, canned	1/2 cup	1	100
Cabbage			
Chinese, raw	1 cup	0	10
green cooked	1/2 cup	0	15
red, raw, shredded	1/2 cup	0	10
Carrot			
cooked	1/2 cup	0	35
raw	1/2 cup	0	30
Cauliflower			
cooked	1/2 cup	0	15
frozen w/ cheese sauce	1/2 cup	6	115
raw	1/2 cup	0	10
Celery			
cooked	1/2 cup	0	10
raw	1 stalk	0	5
Chard, cooked	1/2 cup	0	20
Chilies, green	1/4 cup	0	15
Chinese-style vegetables, frozen	1/2 cup	5	80
Collard greens, cooked	1/2 cup	0	15

Nutritional Information

Food Item	Amount	Fat Gm.	Calories	Food Item	Amount	Fat Gm.	Calories
Vegetables (continued)				knishes	1	3	75
Corn				mashed			
corn on the cob	1 medium	1	80	from flakes	1/2 cup	0	80
cream style, canned	1/2 cup	0	95	w/ milk & margarine	1/2 cup	4	110
frozen, cooked	1/2 cup	0	65	pan fried, O'Brien	1/2 cup	2	80
frozen w/ butter sauce	1/2 cup	3	105	scalloped			
whole kernel, cooked	1/2 cup	1	90	from mix	1/2 cup	6	125
Cucumber				homemade	1/2 cup	5	105
w/ skin	1/2 medium	0	10	w/cheese	1/2 cup	10	175
w/o skin	1/2 cup	0	5	potato pancakes	8" cake	13	400
Eggplant, cooked	1/2 cup	0	15	potato puffs, frozen	1 puff	1	15
Endive lettuce	1 cup	0	10	twice-baked potato w/ cheese	1 medium	10	180
Garbanzo beans	1/2 cup	2	135	Pumpkin, canned	1/2 cup	0	40
Green beans				Radish, raw	10	0	5
French style, cooked	1/2 cup	0	20	Rhubarb, raw	1 cup	0	30
snap, cooked	1/2 cup	0	20	Sauerkraut, canned	1/2 cup	0	20
Hominy, white or yellow,				Scallions, raw	5 medium	0	45
cooked	1 cup	1	140	Soybeans, mature, cooked	1/2 cup	8	150
Italian-style vegetables, frozen	1/2 cup	7	130	Spinach			
Kidney beans	1/2 cup	0	110	cooked	1/2 cup	0	20
Leeks, chopped, raw	1/2 cup	0	35	creamed	1/2 cup	6	90
Lentils, cooked	1/2 cup	0	115	raw	1 cup	0	10
Lettuce, leaf	1/2 cup	0	5	Squash			
Lima beans, cooked	1/2 cup	0	110	acorn, baked	1/2 cup	0	55
Mushrooms				butternut, cooked	1/2 cup	0	40
canned	1/2 cup	0	20	summer			
fried/sauteed	5 medium	10	100	cooked	1/2 cup	0	20
raw	1/2 cup	0	10	raw, sliced	1/2 cup	0	15
Mustard greens, cooked	1/2 cup	0	15	winter, cooked	1/2 cup	0	40
Okra, cooked	1/2 cup	0	25	Sweet potato			
Onions				baked	1 medium	0	120
canned, french fried	1 oz.	15	175	candied	1/2 cup	4	190
chopped, raw	1/2 cup	0	25	mashed w/o fat	1/2 cup	0	170
Parsley, chopped, raw	1/2 cup	0	10	Tofu, raw	4 oz.	5	85
Parsnips, cooked	1/2 cup	0	65	Tomato			
Peas, green, cooked	1/2 cup	0	70	raw	1 medium	0	25
Pepper, bell, chopped, raw	1/2 cup	0	10	stewed	1/2 cup	0	35
Pimientos, canned	3 oz.	0	30	tomato paste, canned	1/2 cup	1	110
Potato				tomato sauce, plain	1/2 cup	0	30
au gratin from mix	1/2 cup	6	140	Turnips, cooked	1/2 cup	0	15
homemade	1/2 cup	9	160	Water chestnuts, canned,			
baked w/ skin	1 medium	0	220	sliced	1/2 cup	0	35
boiled w/o skin	1/2 cup	0	115	Watercress, raw	1/2 cup	0	0
French fries				Wax beans, canned	1/2 cup	0	25
frozen, baked	10 pieces	4	110	Yams, baked	1/2 cup	0	80
homemade, fried	10 pieces	8	160	Zucchini, cooked	1/2 cup	0	15
hash browns	1/2 cup	11	165				

Nutritional Information

Food Item	Amount	Fat Gm.	Calories
Vegetarian/Meatless Items			
Meatless burger	1	0	85
Tempeh	1/2 cup	9	160
Tofu			
Silken soft	3 oz.	3	45
firm	3 oz.	4	65
lowfat	3 oz.	4	85
Vegetable crumbles, frozen	1/2 cup	0	70
Vegetarian hot dog	1	0	80

Note: Nutritional values vary between different brands. The values shown in this book represent an average. Fat gram values have been rounded off to the nearest whole number and calories have been rounded off to the nearest 5.

Fast Food
Nutritional
Values

Fast Food Nutritional Information

Food Item	Amount	Fat Gm.	Calories
Arby's®			
Roast Beef Sandwiches			
Arby's Melt w/Cheddar	1	15	340
Arby-Q®	1	14	360
Beef 'N Cheddar	1	24	480
Big Montana®	1	32	630
Giant Roast Beef	1	23	480
Junior Roast Beef	1	13	310
Regular Roast Beef	1	16	350
Super Roast Beef	1	23	470
Other Sandwiches			
Chicken Bacon 'N Swiss	1	33	610
Chicken Breast Fillet	1	30	540
Chicken Cordon Bleu	1	35	630
Grilled Chicken Deluxe	1	22	450
Roast Chicken Club	1	28	520
Hot Ham 'N Swiss	1	13	340
Sub Sandwiches			
French Dip	1	18	440
Hot Ham 'N Swiss	1	27	530
Italian	1	50	780
Philly Beef 'N Swiss	1	42	700
Roast Beef	1	48	760
Turkey	1	37	630
Market Fresh Sandwiches			
Roast Beef & Swiss	1	42	810
Roast Ham & Swiss	1	34	730
Roast Chicken Caesar	1	38	820
Roast Turkey & Swiss	1	33	760
Roast Turkey Ranch Bacon	1	44	880
Market Fresh Ultimate BLT	1	49	820
Market Fresh Salads (dressings not included)			
Turkey Club Salad	1	21	350
Caesar Salad	1	4	90
Grilled Chicken Caesar	1	8	230
Chicken Finger Salad	1	34	570
Caesar Side Salad	1	2	45
Light Menu			
Light Grilled Chicken	1	5	280
Light Roast Chicken Deluxe	1	5	260
Light Roast Turkey Deluxe	1	5	260
Roast Chicken Salad	1	3	160
Grilled Chicken Salad	1	5	210

Food Item	Amount	Fat Gm.	Calories
Garden Salad	1	1	70
Side Salad	1	0	25
Side Items			
Cheddar Curly Fries	1	24	460
Curly Fries SM	1	15	310
Curly Fries M	1	20	400
Curly Fries LG	1	30	620
Homestyle Fries Child-size	1	10	220
Homestyle Fries SM	1	13	300
Homestyle Fries M	1	16	370
Homestyle Fries LG	1	24	560
Potato Cakes	2	16	250
Jalapeno Bites™	1	21	330
Mozzarella Sticks	4	29	470
Onion Petals	1	24	410
Chicken Fngr Snck w/Fries	1	32	580
Chicken Finger	4	38	640
Baked Potato w/Btr/Sr Crm	1	24	500
Broccoli 'N Cheddar BP	1	24	540
Deluxe Baked Potato	1	34	650
Desserts			
Apple Turnover (Iced)	1	16	420
Cherry Turnover (Iced)	1	16	410
Breakfast Items			
Biscuit w/ butter	1	17	280
Biscuit with Ham	1	20	330
Biscuit with Sausage	1	33	440
Biscuit with Bacon	1	21	320
Croissant with Ham	1	19	310
Croissant with Sausage	1	32	420
Croissant with Bacon	1	20	300
Sourdough with Ham	1	7	220
Sourdough with Sausage	1	19	330
Sourdough with Bacon	1	7	380
Add Egg	1	9	110
Add Slice Swiss Cheese	1	3	45
French Toastix (no syrup)	1	17	370
Condiments			
Arby's Sauce® Packet	.5 oz.	0	15
BBQ Dipping Sauce	1 oz.	0	40
Au Jus Sauce	3 oz.	0	5
BBQ Vinaigrette Dressing	2 oz.	11	140
Bleu Cheese Dressing	2 oz.	31	300
Bronco Berry Sauce™	1.5 oz.	0	90

Fast Food Nutritional Information

Food Item	Amount	Fat Gm.	Calories	Food Item	Amount	Fat Gm.	Calories
Arby's ® (continued)			·	**Soups, Salads, Sandwiches**			
Buttermilk Ranch Dressing	2 oz.	39	360	Caesar salad entree	10 oz.	40	470
Buttermilk Rnch Drsng, no fat	2 oz.	0	60	w/o dressing	8 oz.	13	240
Caesar Dressing	2 oz.	34	310	Chicken caesar salad	13 oz.	47	670
Croutons, Cheese & Garlic	.63 oz.	6	100	SW grill chicken salad			
Croutons, Seasoned	.25 oz.	1	30	w/dressing & chips	1 entr	58	890
German Mustard Packet	.25 oz.	0	5	w/o dressing & chips	1 entr	23	470
Honey French Dressing	2 oz.	24	290	Oriental grill chicken salad			
Honey Mustard Sauce	1 oz.	12	130	w/dressing & noodles	1 entr	24	660
Horsey Sauce® Packet	.5 oz.	5	60	w/o dressing & noodles	1 entr	10	320
Italian Dressing	2 oz.	1	25	Chicken sandwich/			
Italian Parmesan Dressing	2 oz.	24	240	cheese sauce	1	32	760
Ketchup Packet	.32 oz.	0	10	w/o cheese sauce	1	4	430
French Toast Syrup	.5 oz.	0	130	Chicken salad sandwich	1	33	680
Mayonnaise Packet				Chicken noodle soup	3/4 cup	5	100
Regular	.44 oz.	10	90	Chicken tortilla soup	3/4 cup	8	170
Light, Cholesterol-Free	.44 oz.	2	20	w/o toppings	3/4 cup	5	80
Marinara Sauce	1.5 oz.	1	35	Turkey tortilla soup	3/4 cup	7	160
Tangy Southwest Sauce™	1.5 oz.	26	250	w/o toppings	3/4 cup	4	70
Thousand Island Dressing	2 oz.	28	290	BBQ grilled chicken sand.	1	45	830
				w/o cheese or mayo	1	15	550
Beverages				Marinated grilled chicken sand.	1	36	670
Milk	1	5	120	w/o mayo	1	13	470
Hot Chocolate	1	1	110	Turkey sandwich			
Orange Juice	1	0	140	cheese & sauce	1	26	630
Vanilla Shake	1	15	470	w/o cheese & sauce	1	4	400
Chocolate Shake	1	16	480	Ham sandwich			
Strawberry Shake	1	13	500	w/ cheese & sauce	1	32	660
Jamocha Shake	1	15	470	w/o cheese & sauce	1	9	450
				Ham & turkey club			
Boston Market®				w/ cheese & sauce	1	43	890
				w/o cheese & sauce	1	6	430
Entrees				Meat loaf sandwich			
Chicken				w/ cheese	1	29	730
white meat, no skin or wing	1/4 chkn	4	160	w/o cheese	1	21	690
white meat w/ skin	1/4 chkn	12	280	Open faced meatloaf sandwich			
dark meat, no skin	1/4 chkn	10	210	w/ potatoes & gravy	1	36	730
dark meat w/ skin	1/4 chkn	22	330	Turkey bacon club	1	37	770
1/2 chicken w/ skin	1/2 chkn	37	630	Open faced turkey	1	20	720
marinated grilled chicken	1 breast	10	230				
grilled chicken, BBQ	1 entree	19	400	**Hot Side Dishes**			
grilled chicken teriyaki	1 entree	10	290	Steamed vegetables	2/3 cup	1	35
chicken pot pie	1 pie	46	750	New potatoes	3/4 cup	3	140
chicken salad	3/4 cup	30	390	Buttered corn	3/4 cup	4	190
Turkey breast, skinless, rotiss.	5 oz.	1	170	Green beans	3/4 cup	4	70
Ham w/ cinnamon apples	8 oz.	13	520	Green bean casserole	3/4 cup	5	80
Meat loaf & chunky tomato sc	8 oz.	18	370	Sweet potato casserole	3/4 cup	13	280
Meat loaf & brown gravy	7 oz.	22	390				

Fast Food Nutritional Information

Food Item	Amount	Fat Gm.	Calories
Boston Market (continued)			
Zucchini marinara	3/4 cup	4	80
Mashed potatoes	2/3 cup	8	180
w/ gravy	3/4 cup	9	200
Chicken gravy	1 oz.	1	15
Rice pilaf	2/3 cup	5	180
Creamed spinach	3/4 cup	20	260
Stuffing	3/4 cup	8	190
Butternut squash	3/4 cup	6	160
Macaroni & cheese	3/4 cup	10	280
BBQ baked beans	3/4 cup	9	330
Cinnamon apples	3/4 cup	5	250
Cold Side Dishes			
Fruit salad	3/4 cup	1	70
Mediterranean pasta salad	3/4 cup	10	170
Cranberry relish	3/4 cup	5	370
Tortellini salad	3/4 cup	24	380
Caesar side salad	4 oz.	26	300
Chunky chicken salad	3/4 cup	39	480
Cole slaw	3/4 cup	19	300
Jumpin juice squares	1 side	0	150
Old-fashioned potato salad	1 side	12	200
Baked Goods			
Brownie	1	23	580
Corn bread	1 loaf	6	200
Oatmeal raisin cookie	1	20	390
Chocolate chip cookie	1	19	390
Peanut butter cookie	1	25	420
Apple struesel pie	1 slice	15	460
Cherry struesel pie	1 slice	14	360
Pecan pie	1 slice	24	500
Pumpkin pie	1 slice	9	290
Cheesecake	1 slice	40	600
Chocolate cake	1 slice	32	650
Hummingbird cake	1 slice	36	710
Burger King®			
Breakfast			
Croissan'wich w/ bcn., egg/ chs.	1	24	350
Croissan'wich w/ sg., egg & chs.	1	41	530
Croissan'wich w/ ham, egg/chs.	1	22	350
Egg'wich™			
w/Canadian bacon			
egg, & cheese	1	23	420
w/Canadian bacon/egg	1	19	380
w/egg & cheese	1	23	410

Food Item	Amount	Fat Gm.	Calories
French Toast Sticks	1 serving	27	500
Hash Browns	1 serving	12	220
A.M. Express Jam			
grape	1 pkg.	0	30
strawberry	1 pkg.	0	30
Burgers			
Whopper	1	39	640
Whopper w/ cheese	1	46	730
Double Whopper	1	56	870
Double Whopper w/ cheese	1	63	960
Whopper Jr.	1	24	420
Whopper Jr. w/ cheese	1	28	460
Hamburger	1	15	330
Cheeseburger	1	19	380
Double Cheeseburger	1	36	600
Dble Cheeseburger w/ bacon	1	39	640
Homestyle griller	1	27	480
Smokehouse cheddar™	1	48	720
King Supreme™	1	34	550
Quarter pounder	1	21	490
Sandwich/Side Orders			
BK Big Fish Sandwich	1	43	720
BK Broiler Chicken Sandwich	1	29	540
Chicken Sandwich	1	43	700
Chicken Tenders	6 pieces	12	250
Broiled Chick. Salad w/o drsg.	1	10	200
Garden Salad w/o dressing	1	5	90
Side Salad	1	3	50
French Fries (medium)	1 serving	20	400
Onion Rings	1 serving	14	310
Desserts			
Dutch apple pie	1	14	340
Hershey's® sundae pie	1	18	310
Hot fudge brownie royale	1	19	440
Fresh baked cookies	1 serving	21	440
Dairy Queen®			
DQ Brazier Entrees			
Single Hamburger	1	13	310
Single hamburger w/cheese	1	18	365
Double hamburger	1	25	460
Double hamburger w/cheese	1	34	570
Homestyle® Ultimate burger	1	47	700
Hot dog	1	16	280
Hot dog w/ cheese	1	21	330

Fast Food Nutritional Information

Food Item	Amount	Fat Gm.	Calories
Dairy Queen ® (continued)			
Hot dog w/ chili	1	19	320
1/4 pound Super Dog	1	38	590
BBQ beef sandwich	1	9	300
Grilled chicken fillet sandwich	1	8	300
Breaded chicken fillet sandwich	1	20	430
w/cheese	1	25	480
Fish fillet sandwich	1	16	370
w/cheese	1	21	420
Salads & Sides			
Side salad without dressing	1 serving	0	25
Garden salad	1 serving	13	200
Thousand Island dressing	2 oz.	21	225
Reduced calorie French drsg	2 oz.	5	90
French fries			
small	1 serving	12	300
medium	1 serving	15	380
large	1 serving	19	480
Onion rings	1 serving	30	470
Desserts			
Vanilla cone			
small	1 serving	7	230
medium	1 serving	9	330
large	1 serving	15	480
Chocolate cone			
small	1 serving	8	240
medium	1 serving	11	340
Chocolate dipped cone, med.	1 serving	24	450
Chocolate sundae, regular	1 serving	10	400
Vanilla shake			
regular	1 serving	14	520
large	1 serving	16	600
Chocolate shake, small	1 serving	14	540
Vanilla malt, regular	1 serving	14	610
Banana split	1 serving	11	510
Peanut Buster(R) Parfait	1 serving	32	710
Hot Fudge Brownie Delight®	1 serving	29	710
Nutty Double Fudge-	1 serving	22	580
Strawberry Blizzard®			
small	1 serving	12	400
regular	1 serving	16	570
Small Heath Blizzard®	1 serving	23	560
Heath Blizzard®, regular	1 serving	36	820
Strbry. Waffle Cone Sundae™	1 serving	12	350
Buster Bar®	1 serving	29	450
Dilly® Bar	1 serving	13	210
DQ® Sandwich	1 serving	4	140

Food Item	Amount	Fat Gm.	Calories
DQ® Frozen Cake Slice	1 serving	18	380
Mr. Misty®, regular	1 serving	0	250
Yogurt Cone			
regular	1 serving	1	180
large	1 serving	1	260
Yogurt, cup			
regular	1 serving	1	170
large	1 serving	1	230
Yogurt strawberry sundae, reg.	1 serving	1	200
Strawberry Breeze®			
regular	1 serving	1	420
small	1 serving	1	290
Heath Breeze®			
regular	1 serving	21	680
small	1 serving	12	450
DQ Big Scoop®			
chocolate	1 serving	14	310
vanilla	1 serving	14	300
Domino's® Pizza			
12"Thin Crust			
Cheese	1/3 pizza	16	365
Pepperoni	1/3 pizza	23	450
Extra cheese & pepperoni	1/3 pizza	28	510
Ham	1/3 pizza	17	390
Italian sausage & mushroom	1/3 pizza	21	440
Veggie	1/3 pizza	17	385
12" Deep Dish			
Cheese	1/4 pie	24	560
Pepperoni	1/4 pie	29	620
Extra cheese & pepperoni	1/4 pie	33	670
Ham	1/4 pie	25	575
Italian sausage & mushroom	1/4 pie	28	620
Veggie	1/4 pie	25	575
12" Hand Tossed			
Cheese	1/4 pie	10	345
Pepperoni	1/4 pie	15	405
Extra Cheese & Pepperoni	1/4 pie	19	455
Ham	1/4 pie	10	360
Italian sausage & mushroom	1/4 pie	14	400
Veggie	1/4 pie	10	360
Kentucky Fried Chicken®			
Chicken			
Original Recipe®			
Whole Wing	1	9	145
Breast	1	19	370

Fast Food Nutritional Information

Food Item	Amount	Fat Gm.	Calories
Kentucky Fried Chicken ® (continued)			
Drumstick	1	8	140
Thigh	1	25	360
Extra Crispy™			
Whole Wing	1	12	190
Breast	1	28	470
Drumstick	1	10	160
Thigh	1	26	370
Hot & Spicy			
Whole Wing	1	11	180
Breast	1	27	450
Drumstick	1	9	140
Thigh	1	28	390
Sandwiches			
Original Recipe®			
w/ sauce	1	22	450
w/o sauce	1	13	360
Triple Crunch®			
w/ sauce	1	37	560
w/o sauce	1	15	390
Triple Crunch® Zinger			
w/sauce	1	40	640
w/o sauce	1	23	460
Tender Roast®			
w/ sauce	1	19	400
w/o sauce	1	5	270
Honey BBQ Flavored	1	6	310
Twister®	1	38	670
Blazin Twister®	1	43	720
Crispy Caesar Twister®	1	41	745
Honey BBQ Crunch Melt	1	25	555
Crispy Strips			
Colonels Crispy Strips®	3	24	400
Spicy Crispy Strips	3	15	335
Honey BBQ Strips	3	15	375
Blazin Strips	3	16	315
Popcorn Chicken			
Popcorn Chicken - Small	1	30	450
Popcorn Chicken - Large	1	40	620
Pot Pie			
Chunky Chicken	1	48	830
Wings			
Hot Wings™ Pieces	6	33	470
Honey BBQ Wings w/ sce	6	38	605

Food Item	Amount	Fat Gm.	Calories
Vegetables			
Mashed Potatoes			
w/Gravy	1 serving	6	120
Potato Wedges	1	15	375
Mac & Cheese	1 serving	8	180
Corn on the Cob	1	2	150
BBQ Baked Beans	1 serving	3	190
Cole Slaw	1 serving	14	230
Potato Salad	1 serving	14	230
Green Beans	1 serving	2	45
Mean Greens®	1 serving	3	70
Breads			
Biscuits	1	10	180
Desserts			
Choc. Chip Cake	1 piece	16	320
Parfait - Fudge Brownie	1	10	280
Parfait - Lemon Creme	1	14	410
Parfait - Chocolate Crm	1	15	290
Parfait - Straw. Shortcake	1	7	200
Pecan Pie Slice	1 slice	23	490
Apple Pie Slice	1 slice	14	310
Strawberry Crm Pie	1 slice	15	280
McDonald's®			
Sandwiches			
Big Mac®	1	34	590
Big N' Tasty®	1	32	530
Big N' Tasty® with Cheese	1	37	580
Cheeseburger	1	14	330
Chicken McGrill® w/o dressing	1	4	260
Crispy Chicken	1	26	500
Double Cheeseburger	1	27	480
Dbl Qtr Pnder® w/Cheese	1	48	760
Filet-O-Fish®	1	26	470
Grilled Chicken Flatbread	1	22	520
Hamburger	1	10	280
Hot 'n Spicy McChicken®	1	26	450
McChicken®	1	23	430
Qtr Pounder ® w/cheese	1	30	530
Quarter Pounder®	1	21	420
Side Items			
Large French Fries	1	26	540
McValue French Fries	1	16	320
Medium French Fries	1	22	450
Small French Fries	1	10	210

Fast Food Nutritional Information

Food Item	Amount	Fat Gm.	Calories
McDonald's ® (continued)			
Super Size® French Fries	1 serving	29	610
Barbeque Sauce	1 pkg	0	45
Chicken McNuggets®			
4 piece	4	13	210
6 piece	6	20	310
10 piece	10	33	510
Sauces			
Honey	1 pkg	0	45
Honey Mustard Sauce	1 pkg	5	50
Hot Mustard Sauce	1 pkg	4	60
Light Mayonnaise	1 pkg	5	45
Sweet 'N Sour Sauce	1 pkg	0	50
Salads			
McSalad® Shaker			
Chef Salad	1	8	150
Garden Salad	1	6	90
Grilled Chick. Caesar Salad	1	3	100
Side Caesar Salad	1	2	35
Side Garden Salad	1	2	35
1000 Island Dressing	1 pkg	9	130
Caesar Dressing	1 pkg	13	150
Fat Free Herb Vinaigrette	1 pkg	0	35
Honey Mustard Dressing	1 pkg	11	160
Ranch Dressing	1 pkg	18	170
Red French Dressing	1 pkg	6	130
Breakfast			
Bacon, Egg & Cheese Biscuit	1	31	480
Bagel (plain)	1	1	260
Big Breakfast	1	48	710
Biscuit	1	11	240
Egg McMuffin®	1	12	300
English Muffin	1	2	150
Ham, Egg & Cheese Bagel	1	23	550
Hash Browns	1	8	130
Hotcakes (marg. & syrup)	1 serving	17	600
Sausage	1 serving	16	170
Sausage Biscuit	1	28	410
Sausage Biscuit with Egg	1	33	490
Sausage Breakfast Burrito	1	16	290
Sausage McMuffin®	1	23	370
Sausage McMuffin® w/Egg	1	28	450
Scrambled Eggs	2	11	160
Spanish Omelette Bagel	1	40	710
Steak, Egg & Cheese Bagel	1	35	700

Food Item	Amount	Fat Gm.	Calories
Desserts			
Apple Danish	1	15	340
Cheese Danish	1	21	400
Cinnamon Roll	1	15	340
Baked Apple Pie	1 slice	13	260
Butterfinger ® McFlurry™	12 oz.	22	620
Butterfinger ® McFlurry™	16 oz.	31	900
Chocolate Chip Cookie	1	9	170
Choc. Triple Thick™ Shake	12 fl oz.	12	430
Choc. Triple Thick™ Shake	16 fl oz.	17	580
Choc. Triple Thick™ Shake	21 fl oz.	22	750
Choc. Triple Thick™ Shake	32 fl oz.	33	1150
Fruit 'n Yogurt Parfait			
w/granola	11.9 oz.	5	380
w/o granola	10.9 oz.	4	280
Hot Caramel Sundae	6.4 oz.	10	360
Hot Fudge Sundae	6.3 oz.	12	340
M&M® McFlurry™	12 oz.	23	630
M&M® McFlurry™	16 oz.	33	910
Chocolate Chip Cookies	1 serving	14	280
McDonaldland® Cookies	1 serving	8	230
Nestle Crunch® McFlurry™	12 oz.	24	630
Nestle Crunch® McFlurry™	16 oz.	35	920
Nuts (for Sundaes)	0.3 oz.	4	40
Oreo® McFlurry™	12 oz.	20	570
Oreo® McFlurry™	16 oz.	29	820
Snack Size Fruit 'n Yogurt Parfait			
w/granola	5.3 oz.	2	160
w/o granola	5.0 oz.	2	130
Strawberry Sundae	6.3 oz.	7	290
Straw. Triple Thick™ Shake	12 fl oz.	12	420
Straw. Triple Thick™ Shake	16 fl oz.	16	560
Straw. Triple Thick™ Shake	21 fl oz.	21	730
Straw. Triple Thick™ Shake	32 fl oz.	32	1120
Vanilla Ice Cream Cone	1	5	150
Vanilla Triple Thick™ Shake	12 fl oz.	12	430
Vanilla Triple Thick™ Shake	16 fl oz.	16	570
Vanilla Triple Thick™ Shake	21 fl oz.	21	750
Vanilla Triple Thick™Shake	32 fl oz.	32	1140
Beverages			
1% Lowfat Milk	8.0 fl oz.	3	100
Coca-Cola Classic®	12 fl oz.	0	110
Coca-Cola Classic®	16 fl oz.	0	150
Coca-Cola Classic®	21 fl oz.	0	210

Fast Food Nutritional Information

Food Item	Amount	Fat Gm.	Calories	Food Item	Amount	Fat Gm.	Calories
McDonald's ® (continued)				pan	1 slice	14	290
Coca-Cola Classic®	32 fl oz.	0	310	Stuffed Crust	1 slice	16	360
Coca-Cola Classic®	42 fl oz.	0	410	Stuffed Crust Gold	1 slice	20	440
Coffee	8 fl oz.	0	0	The Big New Yorker™	1 slice	18	410
Coffee	12 fl oz.	0	5	Beef			
Coffee	16 fl oz.	0	10	Thin 'N Crispy®	1 slice	15	270
Diet Coke®	12 fl oz.	0	0	hand tossed	1 slice	17	330
Diet Coke®	16 fl oz.	0	0	pan	1 slice	18	330
Diet Coke®	21 fl oz.	0	0	Stuffed Crust	1 slice	18	390
Diet Coke®	32 fl oz.	0	0	Stuffed Crust Gold	1 slice	24	490
Diet Coke®	42 fl oz.	0	0	The Big New Yorker™	1 slice	26	500
Half & Half Creamer	.4 fl oz.	2	15	Ham			
Hi-C® Orange Drink	12 fl oz.	0	120	Thin 'n Crispy®	1 slice	7	180
Hi-C® Orange Drink	16 fl oz.	0	160	hand tossed	1 slice	10	260
Hi-C® Orange Drink	21 fl oz.	0	240	pan	1 slice	12	260
Hi-C® Orange Drink	32 fl oz.	0	350	Stuffed Crust	1 slice	13	330
Hi-C® Orange Drink	42 fl oz.	0	460	Stuffed Crust Gold	1 slice	17	410
Iced Tea	12 fl oz.	0	0	The Big New Yorker™	1 slice	14	370
Iced Tea	16 fl oz.	0	0	Pepperoni			
Iced Tea	21 fl oz.	0	0	Thin 'n Crispy®	1 slice	10	215
Iced Tea	32 fl oz.	0	0	hand tossed	1 slice	13	280
Iced Tea	42 fl oz.	0	0	pan	1 slice	12	265
Orange Juice	12 oz.	0	140	Stuffed Crust	1 slice	16	360
Orange Juice	16 oz.	0	180	Stuffed Crust Gold	1 slice	20	430
Orange Juice	21 oz.	0	250	The Chicago Dish™	1 slice	20	390
Sprite®	12 fl oz.	0	110	The Big New Yorker™	1 slice	17	390
Sprite®	16 fl oz.	0	150	Italian Sausage			
Sprite®	21 fl oz.	0	210	Thin'n Crispy®	1 slice	17	290
Sprite®	32 fl oz.	0	310	hand tossed	1 slice	18	340
Sprite®	42 fl oz.	0	410	pan	1 slice	20	340
Panda Express				Stuffed Crust	1 slice	20	400
Chicken with mushrooms	5 oz.	9	170	Stuffed Crust Gold	1 slice	27	520
Beef and Broccoli	5 oz.	11	180	The Chicago Dish™	1 slice	22	410
Orange Chicken	5 oz.	13	310	The Big New Yorker™	1 slice	20	530
Spicy Chicken with peanuts	5 oz.	29	510	Pork			
Sweet and Sour Pork w/ Sce	6 oz.	20	370	Thin'n Crispy®	1 slice	14	270
Vegetable Chow Mein	8 oz.	10	300	hand tossed	1 slice	16	320
Lo Mein	8 oz.	10	270	pan	1 slice	17	320
Vegetable Fried Rice	8 oz.	19	410	Stuffed Crust	1 slice	18	380
Egg Flower Soup	1 1/2 cup	0	80	Stuffed Crust Gold	1 slice	25	500
Hot and Sour Soup	1 1/2 cup	4	110	The Big New Yorker™	1 slice	25	490
Egg Roll	2	6	190	Meat Lover's®			
Pizza Hut®				Thin'n Crispy®	1 slice	19	310
Cheese				hand tossed	1 slice	17	310
Thin 'N Crispy®	1 slice	8	205	pan	1 slice	18	340
hand tossed	1 slice	7	235	Stuffed Crust	1 slice	27	550
				The Chicago Dish™	1 slice	27	470

Fast Food Nutritional Information

Food Item	Amount	Fat Gm.	Calories
Pizza Hut ® (continued)			
Veggie Lover's			
Thin'n Crispy®	1 slice	7	185
hand tossed	1 slice	6	215
pan	1 slice	10	240
Stuffed Crust	1 slice	14	340
The Chicago Dish™	1 slice	18	370
Pepperoni Lover's®			
Thin 'N Crispy®	1 slice	16	285
hand tossed	1 slice	14	305
pan	1 slice	17	330
Stuffed Crust	1 slice	21	420
Supreme			
Thin 'N Crispy®	1 slice	13	255
hand tossed	1 slice	12	280
pan	1 slice	15	310
Stuffed Crust	1 slice	20	410
The Chicago Dish™	1 slice	23	420
Stuffed Crust Gold	1 slice	24	490
The Big New Yorker™	1 slice	23	470
Personal Pan Pizza			
Pepperoni	whl. pizza	28	635
Supreme	whl. pizza	34	720
Subway®			
Classic Sandwiches			
6" BMT®	1	24	480
6" Cold Cut Trio	1	21	440
6" Meatball	1	26	530
6" Seafood & Crab®	1	16	410
6" Steak & Cheese	1	14	390
6" SUBWAY Melt	1	16	410
6" Tuna	1	22	450
Select Sandwiches			
6" Swt Onion Chick. Teriyaki	1	5	380
6" Red Wine Vinaig. Club	1	6	350
6" Honey Mustard Ham	1	5	310
6" Dijon Horseradish Melt	1	22	470
6" Southwest Turkey Bacon	1	17	410
7 Under 6 Sandwiches			
6" Ham	1	5	290
6" Roast Beef	1	5	290
6" Roasted Chicken Breast	1	5	320
6" SUBWAY Club®	1	6	320

Food Item	Amount	Fat Gm.	Calories
6" Turkey Breast	1	5	280
6" Turkey Breast & Ham	1	5	290
6" Veggie Delite®	1	3	230
Deli Sandwiches			
Ham	1	4	210
Roast Beef	1	5	220
Tuna	1	16	330
Turkey Breast	1	4	220
Breakfast Sandwich			
Cheese & Egg	1	15	320
Bacon & Egg	1	16	320
Ham & Egg	1	14	340
Western Egg	1	12	300
Steak & Egg	1	14	330
Taco Bell®			
Tacos			
Taco	1	10	170
Taco Supreme®	1	14	220
Soft Taco - Beef	1	10	210
Soft Taco - Chicken	1	6	190
Soft Taco Supreme® Beef	1	14	260
Soft Taco Supreme® Chicken	1	10	230
Grilled Steak Soft Taco	1	17	280
Double Decker® Taco	1	14	340
Double Decker® Taco Supr	1	18	380
Burritos			
Bean Burrito	1	10	370
7-Layer Burrito	1	22	530
Chili Cheese Burrito	1	18	390
Burrito Supreme®			
Beef	1	18	440
Chicken	1	14	410
Steak	1	16	420
Fiesta Burrito			
Beef	1	15	390
Chicken	1	12	370
Steak	1	13	370
Grilled Stuft Burrito			
Beef	1	33	730
Chicken	1	26	680
Steak	1	28	680

Fast Food Nutritional Information

Food Item	Amount	Fat Gm.	Calories
Taco Bell ® (continued)			
Chalupas			
Chalupa Supreme			
Beef	1	24	390
Chicken	1	20	370
Steak	1	22	370
Chalupa Baja			
Beef	1	27	430
Chicken	1	24	400
Steak	1	25	400
Chalupa Nacho Cheese			
Beef	1	22	380
Chicken	1	18	350
Steak	1	19	350
Gorditas			
Gordita Supreme®			
Beef	1	16	310
Chicken	1	12	290
Steak	1	13	290
Gordita Baja®			
Beef	1	19	350
Chicken	1	15	320
Steak	1	16	340
Gordita Nacho Cheese			
Beef	1	13	300
Chicken	1	10	270
Steak	1	11	270
Side Items			
Tostada	1	10	250
Mexican Pizza	1	31	550
Enchirito®			
Beef	1	18	380
Chicken	1	14	350
Steak	1	16	360
MexiMelt®	1	16	290
Taco Salad			
w/ Salsa	1	42	790
w/ Salsa w/o Shell	1	21	420
Express w/ Chips	1	31	620
Quesadilla			
Cheese	1	28	490
Chicken	1	30	540
Steak	1	31	540
Extreme Cheese	1	25	470

Food Item	Amount	Fat Gm.	Calories
Zesty Chicken Border Bowl™			
w/Dressing	1	42	730
w/o Dressing	1	19	500
Southwest Steak Bowl	1	32	700
Nachos	1	19	320
Nachos Supreme	1	26	450
Nachos BellGrande®	1	43	780
Pintos'n Cheese	1 serving	7	180
Mexican Rice	1 serving	10	210
Cinnamon Twists	1 serving	5	160
Breakfast			
Breakfast Gordita	1	24	380
Breakfast Burrito	1	25	510
Breakfast Steak Burrito	1	26	500
Breakfast Quesadilla			
w/o Green Sauce	1	20	400
w/Green Sauce	1	23	460
Sauces			
Border Sauce - Mild	1 pkt.	0	5
Border Sauce - Hot	1 pkt.	0	10
Border Sauce - Fire	1 pkt.	0	15
Red Sauce	1 serving	0	10
Green Sauce	1 serving	0	10
Nacho Cheese Sauce	1 serving	4	50
Pepper Jack Cheese	1 serving	15	150
Fiesta Salsa	1 serving	0	5
Sour Cream	1 serving	5	60
Guacamole	1 serving	4	50
Cheddar Cheese	1 serving	9	110
Three Cheese Blend	1 serving	8	100
Creamy Lime Sauce	1 serving	19	180
Creamy Jalapeno Sauce	1 serving	14	140
Zesty Dressing	1 serving	16	160
Wendy's®			
Sandwiches			
Classic Single® Everything	1 ea.	19	410
Big Bacon Classic ®	1 ea.	20	570
Jr. Hamburger	1 ea.	9	270
Jr. Cheeseburger	1 ea.	12	310
Jr. Bacon Cheeseburger	1 ea.	18	380
Jr. Cheeseburger Deluxe	1 ea.	16	350
Hamburger, Kids' Meal	1 ea.	9	270
Cheeseburger, Kids' Meal	1 ea.	12	310

Fast Food Nutritional Information

Food Item	Amount	Fat Gm.	Calories	Food Item	Amount	Fat Gm.	Calories
Wendy's® (continued)				**Additional Salad Dressings**			
Grilled Chicken Sandwich	1 ea.	7	300	Blue Cheese	1 pkt.	30	290
Chicken Breast Fillet Sand.	1 ea.	16	430	Creamy Ranch	1 pkt.	25	250
Chicken Club Sandwich	1 ea.	19	470	Fat Free French Style	1 pkt.	0	90
Spicy Chicken Sandwich	1 ea.	15	430	Low Fat Honey Mustard	1 pkt.	4	120
Sandwich Components				Reduced Fat Creamy Ranch	1 pkt.	9	110
1/4 lb. Hamburger Patty	1/4 lb.	14	200	**Potatoes, Chili, & Nuggets**			
2 oz. Hamburger Patty	2 oz.	7	100	French Fries			
Grilled Chicken Fillet	1 pc.	4	110	Kids' Meal	3.2 oz.	11	250
Breaded Chicken Fillet	1 pc.	11	230	Medium	5.0 oz.	17	390
Spicy Chicken Fillet	1 pc.	10	230	Biggie®	5.6 oz.	19	440
Kaiser Bun	1 ea.	3	200	Great Biggie®	6.7 oz.	23	530
Sandwich Bun	1 ea.	2	160	Hot Stuffed Baked Potatoes			
American Cheese	1 sl.	5	70	Plain	10 oz.	0	310
American Cheese, Jr.	1 sl.	4	45	Bacon & Cheese	1 ea.	22	580
Bacon	1 str.	2	20	Broccoli & Cheese	1 ea.	14	480
Honey Mustard Sauce	1 tsp.	2	25	Sour Cream & Chives	1 ea.	6	370
Ketchup	1 tsp.	0	10	Country Crock® Spread	1 pkt.	7	60
Lettuce	1 leaf	0	0	Chili			
Mayonnaise	1-1/2 tsp.	3	30	Small	8 oz.	6	200
Mustard	1/2 tsp.	0	0	Large	12 oz.	9	300
Onion	4 rings	0	5	Cheddar Cheese, shredded	2 T.	6	70
Dill Pickles	4 ea.	0	0	Saltine Crackers	2 ea.	1	25
Tomatoes	1 sl.	0	5	Hot Chili Seasoning	1 pkt.	0	5
Fresh Salads				Crispy Chicken Nuggets™			
Caesar Side Salad	1 ea.	4	70	5 Piece	1	14	220
Homestyle Garlic Croutons	1 pkt.	3	70	4 Piece Kids' Meal	1	11	180
Caesar Dressing	1 pkt.	16	150	Barbecue Sauce	1 pkt.	0	40
Side Salad	1 ea.	0	35	Honey Mustard Sauce	1 pkt.	12	130
Chicken BLT Salad	1 ea.	16	310	Sweet & Sour Sauce	1 pkt.	0	45
Homestyle Garlic Croutons	1 pkt.	3	70	**Frosty and Soft Drinks**			
Honey Mustard Dressing	1 pkt.	29	310 ·	Frosty™			
Mandarin Chicken™ Salad	1 ea.	2	150	Junior	6 oz.	4	170
Roasted Almonds	1 pkt.	12	130	Small	12 oz.	8	330
Crispy Rice Noodles	1 pkt.	2	60	Medium	16 oz.	11	440
Oriental Sesame Dressing	1 pkt.	21	280	Beverages			
Spring Mix Salad	1 ea.	11	180	Cola Soft Drink	11 oz.	0	140
Honey Roasted Pecans	1 pkt.	13	130	Diet Cola Soft Drink	11 oz.	0	0
House Vinaig. Dressing	1 pkt.	20	220	Lemon-Lime Soft Drink	11 oz.	0	130
Taco Supremo Salad	1 ea.	17	360				
Taco Chips	1 pkt.	11	220				
Sour Cream	1 pkt.	6	60				
Salsa	1 ea.	0	30				

Recently Added *Fast Food* Items

Fast Food restaurant items are continually changing. We will add new nutritional values as they come available with each new printing of this book.

Food Item	Amount	Fat Gm.	Calories
Arby's®			
Market Fresh Sandwiches			
Roast Ham & Swiss	1	31	700
Chicken Salad	1	44	860
Low Carbys Ultimate BLT Wrap	1	47	650
Low Carbys Roast Turkey/Ranch/Bacon Wrap	1	39	710
Low Carbys Southwest Chicken Wrap	1	30	550
Low Carbys Chicken Caesar Wrap	1	27	520
Market Fresh Salads			
Martha's Vineyard	1	8	250
Santa Fe	1	29	710
Asian Sesame w/o dressing	1	1	140
Garden Side Salad	1	0	35
Loaded Potato Bites™ (Large)	1	44	710
Spicy Cajun Fish Sandwich	1	32	605
Corned Beef Reuben Wrap	1	29	575
Classic Italian Toasted Sub	1	54	950
Philly Beef Toasted Sub	1	37	740
Boston Market			
Broccoli w/Garlic Butter	1	6	80
Market Chopped Salad	1	48	580
Market Chopped Salad Dressing	1	39	360
Roasted Sirloin	3 oz.	6	160
Burger King®			
Burgers			
Angus Steak Burger	1	22	570
Angus Bacon & Cheese Steak Burger	1	33	710
Low Carb Angus Steak Burger	1	18	280
Low Carb Angus Bacon & Cheese Steak Burger	1	29	420
BK Veggie Burger	1	16	380
Chicken Whopper Sandwich Low Carb	1	4	160
Triple Whopper® Sandwich	1	74	1130
BK™ Triple Stacker	1	54	800
BK Veggie™ Burger	1	16	420
Tendergrill™ Chicken Garden Salad	1	9	240

Food Item	Amount	Fat Gm.	Calories
Diary Queen®			
Salads			
Crispy Chicken Salad w/o dressing	1	20	350
Grilled Chicken Salad w/o dressing	1	10	240
Cappuccino MooLatte®	1	18	500
Mocha MooLatte®	1	31	840
Domino's® Pizza			
12" Thin Crust			
Ham & Pineapple	1 slice	8	150
Green Pepper, Onion & Mushroom	1 slice	8	140
Vegi Feast	1 slice	10	170
Deluxe Feast	1 slice	12	185
Hawaiian Feast	1 slice	10	175
Bacon Cheeseburger Feast	1 slice	15	225
12" Deep Dish			
Ham & Pineapple	1 slice	12	250
Green Pepper, Onion & Mushroom	1 slice	11	245
Vegi Feast	1 slice	14	270
Deluxe Feast	1 slice	15	285
Hawaiian Feast	1 slice	13	275
Bacon Cheeseburger Feast	1 slice	19	325
12" Hand Tossed			
Ham & Pineapple	1 slice	6	200
Green Pepper, Onion & Mushroom	1 slice	6	190
Vegi Feast	1 slice	8	220
Deluxe Feast	1 slice	10	230
Hawaiian Feast	1 slice	8	225
Bacon Cheeseburger Feast	1 slice	13	275
Kentucky Fried Chicken			
Pot Pie Bowls®	1	35	740
Roasted Caesar Salad w/o dressing	1	8	220
KFC Snacker®	1	16	320
Sweet Life Oatmeal Raisin Cookie	1	5	150
McDonalds®			
Salads			
Grilled Chicken Bacon Ranch	1	10	250
Crispy Chicken Bacon Ranch	1	19	350
Bacon Ranch Salad w/o Chicken	1	8	130

Recently Added *Fast Food* Items

Food Item	Amount	Fat Gm.	Calories
Grilled Chicken Caesar	1	6	200
Crispy Chicken Caesar Salad	1	16	310
Caesar Salad w/o Chicken	1	4	90
Grilled Chicken California Cobb	1	11	270
Crispy Chicken California Cobb	1	21	370
California Cobb w/o Chicken	1	9	150
Breakfast			
Sausage Burrito	1	16	290
Warm Cinnamon Roll	1	19	440
Deluxe Warm Cinnamon Roll	1	23	510
Dessert			
Apple Dippers	1	0	35
Low Fat Carmel Dip	1	1	70
Vanilla Reduced Fat Ice Cream Cone	1	5	150
Beverages			
POWERade® Mountain Blast	12 fl oz.	0	70
POWERade® Mountain Blast	16 fl oz.	0	100
POWERade® Mountain Blast	21 fl oz.	0	140
POWERade® Mountain Blast	32 fl oz.	0	200
Ranch Snack Wrap w/Crispy Chicken	1	16	330
Ranch Snack Wrap w/Grilled Chicken	1	10	270
Southwest Salad w/Crispy Chicken	1	16	400
Asian Salad w/Grilled Chicken	1	10	300
Minty Mud Bath Triple Thick® Shake	21 fl oz.	18	760

Subway

Food Item	Amount	Fat Gm.	Calories
Select Sandwiches			
6" Cheese Steak	1	10	360
6" Chipolte Southwest Cheese Steak	1	19	440
6" Italian BMT	1	21	450
Salads			
Garden Fresh	1	1	60
Mediterranean Chicken	1	4	170
Roast Beef	1	3	120
Sweet Onion Chicken Teriyaki	1	3	210
Veggie Delight®	1	1	60
Atkins® Friendly Wrap			
Chicken Bacon Ranch	1	26	440
Mediterranean Chicken	1	18	350
Turkey Bacon Melt	1	27	430

Food Item	Amount	Fat Gm.	Calories
Turkey Breast and Ham	1	23	390
Atkins® Friendly Salads			
Grilled Chicken & Spinach	1	26	420
Classic Club	1	21	390
Breakfast Sandwich			
Vegetable & Egg	1	16	410
Bacon & Egg	1	17	240
Western & Egg	1	14	220
Steak & Egg	1	15	250
Ham & Egg	1	14	230
Vegetable & Egg	1	14	210
French Toast w/syrup	1	8	350
Chipotle Steak & Cheese	1	31	580
Soup			
Roasted Chicken Noodle	1 cup	1	60
Vegetable Beef	1 cup	1	90
Golden Broccoli & Cheese	1 cup	11	180
Cream of Broccoli	1 cup	6	130
Cream of Potato w/bacon	1 cup	11	200
Cheese w/ham and bacon	1 cup	15	240
New England Style Clam Chowder	1 cup	3	110
Minestrone	1 cup	4	90
Chicken and Dumpling	1 cup	4	130
Spanish Style Chicken w/rice	1 cup	2	90
Brown and Wild Rice w/chicken	1 cup	11	190
Chili Con Carne	1 cup	10	240
Tomato Garden Vegetable w/rotini	1 cup	1	100
Beverage			
Fruizle Berry Lishus	1	0	110
Taco Bell			
Steak Grilled Taquitoes	1	7	260
Spicy Chicken Crunchwrap Supreme®	1	23	540
Southwest Steak Border Bowl®	1	24	600
Wendy's			
Black Forest Ham & Swiss Frescata™	1	19	470
Mandarin Orange Cup	1	0	80
Low Fat Strawberry Flavored Yogurt	1	2	140

Fast Food Tips

In today's busy world, fast foods are a great convenience. By checking the food values before ordering, you can have a satisfying meal with a reasonable amount of fat and calories. For breakfasts, try English muffins with jelly or pancakes with syrup. Avoid egg dishes and breakfast sandwiches. Here are some sample lunch and dinner menus that show you how to build your own meal.

	Amt.	Fat g.	Cal.
Burger King®			
Chunky Chicken Salad	1	4	140
Italian dressing, lo-cal	2 T	2	30
Diet cola	1 med.	0	0
Totals		**6**	**170**
Chicken Tenders	6 piece	13	235
Baked potato	1 med.	0	210
Coffee	1	0	0
Totals		**13**	**445**
Hardees®			
Regular roast beef	1	11	270
Side salad	1	0	20
Low-cal dressing	1	1	30
Water	1	0	0
Totals		**12**	**320**
McDonald's®			
McGrilled Chic. Sand.	1	4	260
Side Salad	1	1	30
'Lite' vinaigrette	1/2 pg.	1	25
1% milk	8 oz.	2	100
Totals		**8**	**415**
Chicken fajita	1	8	190
Vanilla yogurt cone	1	1	105
Orange juice	1	0	80
Totals		**9**	**375**

	Amt.	Fat g.	Cal.
Pizza Hut®			
Chunky Veggie, hnd. tsd.	2sl.	12	450
Diet cola	1	0	0
Totals		**12**	**450**
Subway®			
6" turkey sub w/o cheese	1	5	280
Diet Pepsi	1	0	0
Totals		**5**	**280**
Small roast beef salad	1	10	220
2% milk	1	5	120
Totals		**15**	**340**
Taco Bell®			
Chicken Soft Taco	1	6	190
Diet cola	1	0	0
Totals		**6**	**190**
Wendy's®			
Chili	sm.	6	200
Plain baked potato	1 Lrg.	0	310
Iced tea	1	0	0
Totals		**6**	**510**
Chicken Sandwich	1	7	300
Side salad (Garden)	1	0	35
Fat-free dressing	2 T.	0	90
Diet cola	1	0	0
Totals		**7**	**425**

Typical Dinner House/ Family Restaurant Fare

Food Item	Amount	Fat Gm.	Calories
Appetizers			
Buffalo wings with			
4 Tbsp blue cheese	12	80	1010
Fried Mozzarella sticks	9	51	830
Potato skins – loaded	8	79	1120
Main Dishes/Entrees			
Patty melt	1	50	770
Chef Salad with ½ cup			
dressing	5 cups	71	930
Chicken Caesar Salad	4 cups	54	660
Oriental Chicken Salad	5 cups	49	750
Chicken Strips	5	33	625
BBQ Ribs	14	55	775
Mushroom Cheeseburger	1	60	900
Fajitas (guacamole,			
sour cream, Cheese)	4	65	1200
Chicken Stir Fry with rice	3.5 cups	23	700
Sirloin Steak	7 oz.	20	410
Grilled chicken	6 oz.	8	275
Sides			
Baked potato with 2 Tbsp			
sour cream	1	6	330
Coleslaw	1 cup	14	175
French fries	2 cups	30	600
Onion rings	11	65	900
Steamed veggies	1 cup	3	60
Desserts			
Apple pie	1 piece	30	550
Chocolate brownie sundae	11 oz	50	1130
Milkshake	13 oz	30	620

These are average food values for commonly ordered
menu items and will vary slightly from restaurant to restaurant.

How to Make
Better Choices When Eating Out

- Shop carefully for a restaurant that is more likely to accommodate special requests. A telephone call ahead of time can be helpful when choosing a restaurant.

- Don't skip a meal on a day you're going out to eat. In fact, have a light snack an hour or so before leaving home to avoid over-eating at the restaurant.

- Food in the diet or light section of the menu often has far more calories and fat than you might suspect. Look for meals that contain little or no fat, small amounts of meat, poultry, or fish, lots of vegetables and a low fat source of carbohydrates such as a baked potato, rice, or bread.

- Ordering "à la carte" can cost more, but it allows you to eat what you want. Look for appetizers that are broiled, baked, or steamed—not deep-fried in fat.

- Ask your server to clarify unfamiliar terms or to explain how a dish is prepared. Request smaller portions and ask that dressings and sauces be served on the side. Request modified cooking methods (broiling instead of frying, for example).

- Etiquette and nutrition often go hand-in-hand. Don't gulp your food. Chew thoroughly. Eating slowly helps digestion and keeps you from stuffing yourself (it takes 20 minutes before the brain realizes the stomach is full). Practice techniques to extend mealtimes without eating more food: put down your fork between bites, focus on the conversation, or share your meal with a companion. This limits your caloric intake and gives you two meals for the price of one.

- For dessert, share with a friend or take half home. Request sherbet, angel food cake, low-fat yogurt or just an after-dinner mint if you want something sweet at the end of your meal.

• If you choose the salad bar, be careful what you pile on your plate (especially toppings and salad dressing). Survey the entire bar before deciding what's best for you. Start with plenty of lettuce, veggies, and low fat dressing. *Then* add the other goodies; that way you'll be more likely to take less of them. Don't forget that a salad piled high with toppings and dressing can be higher in fat and calories than a meat and potatoes meal! The nutritional low-down on most salad bar favorites is listed below.

Common Salad Bar Ingredients

	Amt	Fat Gm.	Cal.
Avocado	1/4	8	81
Bacon bits	1 T	2	40
Broccoli	1/4 C	0	6
Carrots	1 T	0	1
Cauliflower	1/4 C	0	6
Chedder cheese	1 T	2	29
Cottage cheese 2%	1/2 C	2	102
Cucumbers	1 T	0	2
Garbanzo beans	1 T	0	17
Green pepper	1 T	0	2
Ham chunks	1/4 C	8	120
Hard cooked eggs	1/2	3	39
Mushrooms	1 T	0	0
Olives	5 lg.	2	26
Onions	1 T	0	2
Parmesan cheese	1 T	2	23
Radishes	1 T	0	2
Salad greens	1 C	0	10
Sunflower seeds	1 T	5	52
Tomato	2 sl.	0	5
Turkey chunks	1/4 C	2	70
Dressing			
Blue cheese	2 T	19	180
French	2 T	11	120
Italian	2 T	14	140
Italian, low-cal.	2 T	3	40
Ranch	2 T	15	180
Ranch, low-cal.	2 T	9	120
Thousand Island	2 T	13	130

Low-Fat Low-Calorie *Recipes*

Bon appétit!

Appetizers

Chicken Spread
Makes 1 cup—15 calories & 1 fat gram per tablespoon

1 cup chicken, finely chopped
1 T. crushed pineapple, drained
1/8 tsp. salt

1 T. chopped celery
1/4 tsp. curry powder
1 T. mayo-type dressing

Mix together well. Spread on unsalted whole-grain crackers or in mini pita pockets. Keeps in refrigerator for 3-4 days.

Ham & Cheese Roll-Ups
Serves 4—71 calories & 5 fat grams per serving

2 oz. Neufchatel cheese, softened
2 tsp. low-cal. mayonnaise
1/3 cup alfalfa sprouts

4 slices lean ham
3/4 tsp. prepared mustard

Combine Neufchatel cheese, mayo, and mustard. Spread evenly over ham slices and top with sprouts. Roll up jelly-roll style. Secure with toothpicks in 1-inch increments. Chill. Before serving, slice between toothpicks.

Honey Mustard Chicken Chunks
Serves 6—126 calories & 3 fat grams per 3 chunks

1/4 cup honey
2 T. prepared mustard
1 T. low cal. margarine
2 skinless, boneless chicken breasts, cut into 18 1" chunks

1/2 cup cornflake crumbs
1 tsp. paprika
2 tsp. soy sauce

Microwave honey, mustard, margarine and soy sauce on high for 20 seconds. Divide sauce. Add chicken to one half of the sauce and stir to coat evenly. Combine cornflake crumbs and paprika. Dredge chicken through dry ingredients and discard remaining sauce. Microwave chicken on high for 2 minutes, 9 pieces at a time. Microwave remaining half of sauce on high for 1-1 1/2 minutes. Serve chicken chunks and sauce with a toothpick in each chunk.

Appetizers

Layered Mexican Dip
35 calories & 0 fat grams per serving

8 oz. fat-free cream cheese
8 oz. fat-free sour cream
1 pkg. taco seasoning mix
1 cup chopped lettuce

2 chopped tomatoes
2 gr. onions, chopped finely
8 oz. grated fat-free
cheddar cheese

Blend together cream cheese, sour cream and taco seasoning mix. Spread on a platter. Top with chopped lettuce, tomatoes, green onions and grated cheese. Serve with low-fat taco chips or baked tortillas. Salsa can also be drizzled over top if desired.

Mexican Snack Pizzas
95 calories & 2 fat grams per 1/2 muffin

2 whole-wheat English muffins
1/4 cup kidney beans, drained and chopped
1 T. green pepper, chopped
1/4 cup mozzarella cheese, grated

1/4 cup tomato puree
1 T. chopped onion
1/2 tsp. oregano leaves
1/4 cup shredded lettuce

Split muffins and toast. Mix pureé, beans, onion, green pepper, and oregano. Spread on muffin halves. Sprinkle with cheese. Broil until cheese melts. Garnish with lettuce.

Pineapple Cheese Spread
Makes 1 cup—35 calories & 2 fat grams per tablespoon

6 oz. mozzarella cheese,
  part skim milk
1 T. pineapple juice

1/3 cup crushed pineapple,
  canned & drained

Cut cheese into small pieces. Mix ingredients in blender or food processor, scraping sides often. When mixture is smooth and creamy, serve on unsalted whole-wheat crackers.

Breads

Cheesy Sausage Biscuits

Makes 1 dozen biscuits—68 calories & 2 fat grams

1/4 pound raw turkey sausage
1/2 cup all-purpose flour
1/2 cup unprocessed oat bran
1/2 cup (2 oz.) low cal. grated cheddar cheese

1 tsp. baking powder
1/8 tsp. baking soda
1/2 cup + 3 T. buttermilk
cooking oil spray

Brown sausage, drain. Combine with remaining dry ingredients; add buttermilk, stirring until moistened. Bake spoonfuls of dough on sprayed baking sheet at 450° for 11 minutes.

Herb Corn Bread

Makes 2 loaves—80 calories & 3 fat grams per 1/2" slice

1 cup all-purpose flour
1 cup yellow cornmeal
2 T. sugar
2 tsp. baking powder
2 tsp. fresh, minced thyme
2 tsp. fresh, minced chives
1 1/2 tsp. grated lemon rind
1/8 tsp. salt

1/8 tsp. pepper
1/2 cup corn cut from cob
1 cup non-fat yogurt
3 T. vegetable oil
1 T. water
1 egg, beaten
cooking oil spray

Combine first 10 ingredients. Mix yogurt, oil, water and egg. Stir into flour mixture until moist. Spoon into two lightly sprayed loaf pans. Bake at 400° for 25 minutes.

Oatmeal Muffins

Makes 15 muffins—100 calories & 2 fat grams

1/2 cup shred of wheat brand
1 cup buttermilk
1 cup finely grated carrot
1 T. vegetable oil
2 eggs, beaten
1 cup quick-cooking oats, uncooked

3/4 cup all-purpose flour
1/2 cup packed brown sugar
1 tsp. baking powder
1/2 tsp. baking soda
2 tsp. ground cinnamon
1/4 tsp. salt

Soak cereal in milk for 2 minutes. Add carrot, oil, and eggs, stir. Combine dry ingredients and add to mixture, stirring until moist. Place in double cupcake liners and microwave 6 at a time on high for 2 to 2 1/2 minutes.

Breads

Pumpkin & Oatmeal Bread

Makes 2 loaves—157 calories & 7 fat grams per 1/2" slice

3 cups sifted all-purpose flour	1 cup honey
1 cup oats	1/2 cup vegetable oil
1 T. + 1 tsp. baking powder	4 eggs, lightly beaten
2 tsp. cinnamon	2/3 cup orange juice
1 tsp. baking soda	1 16 oz. can pumpkin
1 tsp. salt	1 cup chopped pecans
1 tsp. ginger	cooking oil spray
1 tsp. mace	1 egg white, lightly beaten
1/4 tsp. ground cloves	1/4 cup oats

Combine dry ingredients. Mix honey, oil, and eggs; add to flour mixture. Add juice, pumpkin, and pecans. Top loaf w/ egg white and oats; bake at 350° 1 hr. in two loaf pans sprayed with cooking spray.

Strawberry Scones

Makes 1 dozen—147 calories & 4 fat grams per scone

2 cups flour	cooking oil spray
1 8-oz. carton vanilla low fat yogurt	1/4 cup sugar
1/4 cup non-swtnd strawberry or raspberry spread	2 tsp. baking powder
1/2 tsp. baking soda	1/4 tsp. salt
3 T. margarine, chilled and cut into small pieces	2 T. finely chopped pecans

Combine dry ingredients, cut in margarine with pastry blender. Stir in yogurt. Knead dough on floured board; pat into 8" circle on sprayed baking sheet. Cut into 12 wedges. Slit each wedge and fill with fruit spread; top w/ pecans. Bake 13 minutes at 400.

Cinnamon Biscuits

Makes 1 dozen—153 calories & 3 fat grams per biscuit

2 cups all-purpose flour	3 T. chilled stick margarine
2 tsp. baking powder	1/2 cup raisins
1 1/2 T. sugar	3/4 cup 1% milk
1/2 tsp. cinnamon	1/2 cup powdered sugar
1/4 tsp. salt	1 T. 1% milk

Mix dry ingredients, cut in margarine. Add raisins & milk; mix. Knead, cut out biscuits. Bake 11 minutes at 450°. Mix powdered sugar and 1 T. milk. Spread over biscuits.

Soups and Salads

Beef-Potato Soup
Makes 5 cups—120 calories & 3 fat grams per 1 1/4 cup serving

1/3 pound ground beef, drained	3 cups water
1 cup sliced onions	1/2 cup chopped celery
salt & pepper to taste	2 tsp. chopped parsley
1 bay leaf	2 whole cloves
1 1/2 cups sliced potatoes	1/2 cup grated carrots

Brown beef; drain fat. Add water, onions, celery, and seasonings. Boil; reduce heat and cook for 30 minutes. Add potatoes, carrots, and parsley. Cook until potatoes are tender, about 15 minutes. Remove bay leaf and cloves before serving.

Luncheon Chicken Salad
Makes 6 1-cup servings— 183 calories & 4 fat grams

2 cups cubed, cooked chicken breast	1 1/2 C. seedless red grapes
1 cup cubed, unpeeled Red Delicious apple	1/4 cup raisins
2/3 cup celery, sliced diagonally	2 T. diced purple onion
1/3 cup plain non-fat yogurt	2 T. low-cal. mayonnaise
1 1/2 T. lemon juice	1/4 tsp. salt
1 T. chopped fresh celery leaves	6 Boston lettuce leaves

Combine chicken, apple, celery, grapes, raisins, and onion in bowl. Blend remaining ingredients and toss with salad. Chill. Serve on individual lettuce-lined serving plates.

Chicken Stew
Makes 4 1-cup servings—175 calories & 2 fat grams

2 chicken breast halves w/o skin	1/2 cup chopped onion
2/3 cup frozen mixed vegetables	1/4 cup sliced celery
2/3 cup diced potatoes	1 cup chopped tomatoes
1/4 tsp. ground thyme	1/8 tsp. pepper
1/4 cup flour	1/4 cup water
1 bayleaf	2 cloves

Cook chicken in water with salt, 2 cloves, and 1 bay leaf for 45 minutes until tender. Cut up meat. Discard leaf and cloves, add water to make 2 cups. Cook veggies in broth for 10 minutes. Add tomatoes and spices. Simmer for 15 minutes. Add chicken. Mix flour and water until smooth. Add to stew, stirring until thickened.

Soups and Salads

Chicken Chutney Salad

Serves 6—259 calories & 5 fat grams per serving

6 cups loosely packed sliced romaine leaves
2 T. chopped almonds
1 1/2 pounds skinned, boned chicken breast
1 9-oz. jar mango chutney

1/2 cup sliced green onions
vegetable cooking spray
1 cup celery, slice diagonally

Toast almonds for 8 minutes in 350° oven; set aside. Spray skillet with oil and cook chicken until done, about 7 minutes per side. Cut across grain into thin slices. Toss chicken, almonds, chutney, onions, and celery all together until well coated. Spoon onto 6 individual lettuce-lined plates.

Vegetable Soup

Makes 4 1-cup servings—70 calories & 0 fat grams

1 cup diced potatoes
1/2 cup chopped onion
1/2 cup sliced carrots
1/4 tsp. oregano leaves
salt and pepper to taste
1 cup tomatoes

1 cup chopped cabbage
1/2 cup diced celery
1/2 cup frozen green beans
1/4 tsp. marjoram leaves
1 bay leaf
2 cups water

Place all ingredients except tomatoes in saucepan and simmer about 10 minutes. Add tomatoes and cook an additional 20 minutes. Discard bay leaf before serving.

Pear & Snow Pea Salad

Serves 4—95 calories & 3 fat grams

1/4 cup plain non-fat yogurt
2 T. unsweetened pineapple juice
3 green onions, thinly sliced
1/2 pound fresh snow peas, trimmed
2 T. chopped, toasted walnuts

1 tsp. lime juice
8 radicchio leaves
1/2 tsp. sugar
1 large firm, ripe pear

Combine yogurt, sugar, and pineapple juice; set aside. Boil snow peas for 15 seconds; cool and pat dry. Cut pear in half lengthwise; core and cut lengthwise again into thin slices. Brush cut sides with lime juice. Arrange snow peas and pears on radicchio-lined salad plates. Drizzle yogurt mixture over top and sprinkle with green onions and walnuts.

Entrees

Tropical Swordfish

Makes 4 servings—178 calories & 5 fat grams

1/2 cup chopped ripe mango	1/4 C. peeled, chopped papaya
2 T. finely chopped celery	1 T. minced fresh parsley
2 tsp. finely chopped purple onion	1 T. lime juice
1 tsp. seeded, minced jalapeno pepper	1 tsp. grated, fresh ginger
2 T. rice vinegar	2 T. Dijon mustard
1 T. + 1 tsp. low sodium soy sauce	4 swordfish steaks

Combine rice vinegar, mustard and soy sauce. Brush over swordfish steaks. Spray grill with cooking oil and grill steaks about 5 minutes per side, or until it flakes easily. While fish cooks, combine remaining ingredients. Serve fish with 1/4 cup mango mixture. Garnish with parsley sprig.

Beef-Vegetable Stir-Fry

Makes 4 3/4-cup servings—180 calories & 6 fat grams

12 oz. beef round steak, boneless	1 tsp. oil
1/2 cup sliced carrots	1/2 cup sliced celery
1/2 cup sliced onions	1 T. soy sauce
1/8 tsp. garlic powder	1 dash pepper
2 cups zucchini, cut into thin strips	2 T. stir-fry sauce or glaze

Brown meat in oil until no longer red. Reduce heat. Add carrots, celery, onion, and seasonings. Cover and cook until carrots are slightly tender, 3-4 minutes. Add squash, cook until vegetables are tender-crisp, 3 to 4 minutes. Add stir-fry glaze. Stir until all is lightly coated with glaze.

Enchilada Casserole

Serves 4—300 calories & 5 fat grams

1/2 cup chopped onion	1/4 cup chopped celery
1/2 cup chopped green pepper	1 cup diced, cooked chicken
1/2 cup canned, drained pinto beans	1/8 tsp. salt
3/4 cup water	1 T. chili powder
1/8 tsp. ground cumin	1/8 tsp. garlic powder
2 cup tomato pureé	1/4 C gr. Monterey Jack cheese
	whole wheat tortillas

Preheat oven to 350°. Simmer onion, green pepper, and celery until tender, drain. Add chicken, beans, and 1/2 the pureé; mix. In baking pan place 4 tortillas, half the filling mixture, and 1/4 of the sauce. Add remaining filling and 1/4 of sauce. Cover with 4 tortillas and remaining sauce. Sprinkle cheese over top. Bake until cheese is melted and sauce bubbly, about 30 minutes.

Entrees

Pork-Sweet Potato Skillet
Serves 4—270 calories and 6 fat grams

4 thin-cut pork chops
1 cup apple juice
1 medium onion, sliced
1 T. flour

1/8 tsp. ground allspice
1/8 tsp. salt
1 17 oz. can sweet potatoes

Brown chops on both sides. Add 3/4 cup apple juice. Top with onion slices. Cover and cook 5 minutes; reduce heat. Mix flour and seasonings. Stir into remaining 1/4 cup apple juice. Stir into pan. Place sweet potatoes in pan, spooning sauce over. Cover and cook an additional 10 minutes, or until chops are done.

Pork & Pepper Stir-Fry
Serves 4—166 calories & 4 fat grams

1 pound pork tenderloin
1 T. low-sodium soy sauce
1/4 tsp. ground ginger
1 cup slivered onion
3/4 cup red pepper, julienne cut
3/4 cup yellow pepper, julienne cut

1 tsp. dark sesame oil
1/4 tsp. garlic powder
1/4 tsp. ground cumin
3/4 cup gr. pepper, julienne
2 T. white wine vinegar

Trim fat from pork and cut cross-wise in 1/4" slices. Stir-fry pork, soy sauce, garlic powder, ginger, and cumin about 3 minutes. Remove pork and set aside. Stir-fry onion and peppers about 5 minutes. Return pork, add vinegar and cook an additional minute.

Pizza
Serves 4—275 calories & 6 fat grams

1 can refrigerated pizza crust
3/4 cup canned tomato pureé (no salt)
1 small onion, sliced
1 cup fresh mushrooms, sliced

1 tsp. oregano leaves
1/2 tsp. garlic powder
1/2 sm. green pepper, sliced
1 cup shredded mozzarella

Preheat oven to 450°. Spread dough on ungreased cookie sheet. Mix pureé and seasonings together, spread evenly over crust. Top with vegetables and sprinkle with cheese. Bake until cheese melts, about 15 minutes.

Entrees

Low-Fat Fried Chicken
Serves 8—220 calories & 11 fat grams

1 3-pound chicken (skinned with bones)	1 tsp. dry parsley
2 egg whites whisked with 2 T. lemon juice	1/2 tsp. paprika
1/2 cup dry whole wheat bread crumbs	1 tsp. rosemary
1/4 cup parmesan cheese	

Remove skin from chicken, rinse and pat dry. Dip chicken pieces in egg white/lemon mixture, then dredge in dry mixture. Spray foil-lined jelly roll pan with non-stick coating. Bake in 400° oven for 40-45 minutes.

Orange-Mustard Glazed Turkey Cutlets
Serves 4—160 calories & 3 fat grams

2 T. frozen orange juice concentrate	4 cloves garlic, crushed
1 tsp. stone-ground mustard	vegetable oil spray
8 turkey cutlets	2 tsp. low-calorie margarine

Combine orange juice with mustard; set aside. Pierce both sides of cutlets with a fork and rub with garlic on both sides. Spray skillet with oil, add margarine and cook cutlets about 2 minutes per side. Turn down heat to low. Add orange juice mixture and stir, thoroughly coating cutlets.

Quick Chili
Serves 4—220 calories & 8 fat grams

1/2 pound lean ground beef (rinsed)	1 T. instant minced onion
1 16-oz. can kidney beans, drained (save liquid)	1 1/2 tsp. chili powder
1/3 cup bean liquid	1 C. tomato pureé, unsalted

Cook beef and drain fat. Add remaining ingredients. Bring to a boil, reduce heat, cover and simmer at least 10 minutes.

Entrees

Individual Meat Loaves

Makes 4 individual loaves—200 calories & 11 fat grams

3/4 pound extra-lean ground beef
1/3 cup crushed wheat crackers
1/2 tsp. basil leaves
1 T. instant minced onion

1 egg
1/3 cup skim milk
1/8 tsp. salt

Preheat oven to 375°. Soak crackers and onion in milk; add egg and seasonings. Mix well. Add ground beef, mix and form into four loaves. Bake in shallow baking pan about 25 minutes or until done. Drain off fat.

Microwaved Stuffed Peppers

Serves 4—215 calories & 12 fat grams

2 green peppers, halved and seeded
boiling water to cover peppers

1/4 cup tomato sauce
meat loaf mixture (above)

Cook peppers in boiling water for 2 minutes. Drain well. Fill pepper halves with meat mixture and place in glass baking dish. Spread 1 T. tomato sauce over each serving. Cover with wax paper. Microwave on high power for 7 minutes. Rotate dish halfway through cooking. Remove from oven and let stand, covered, about 3 minutes.

Aloha Meatballs

Serves 4—245 calories & 11 fat grams

1 recipe meat loaf mixture (top recipe)
1 8 oz. can pineapple chunks, juice packed
1 1/2 tsp. Worcestershire sauce
1/2 cup green pepper, cut into 1" pieces

1 dash pepper
1 T. cornstarch
1 T. water
1/4 tsp. garlic powder

Shape meat mixture into 12 balls. Brown meatballs, about 10 minutes; drain. Drain pineapple, saving juice. Add enough water to juice to make 3/4 cup liquid. Add liquid and seasonings to pan. Boil, reduce heat, cover, and cook an additional 5 minutes. Add pineapple chunks and green pepper. Cook 1 minute. Stir cornstarch and water together; add to pan and stir until thickened.

Side Dishes

Stuffed Baked Potato

Serves 4—155 calories & 0 fat grams

4 baking potatoes   3 T. skim milk
1/2 cup fat-free cottage cheese   1 tsp. dried chopped chives
1/8 tsp. pepper   paprika

Wash and pierce potatoes; bake at 425° for 1 hour. Cut off tops of potatoes lengthwise. Scoop out potatoes, mix with blended cottage cheese, milk, and seasonings. Stuff potato skins, sprinkle with paprika and bake an additional 10 minutes.

Rice-Pasta Pilaf

Serves 4—135 calories & 4 fat grams

1/3 cup uncooked brown rice   2 T. chopped mushrooms
1 1/2 cup unsalted chicken broth   1/2 clove minced garlic
2 tsp. margarine   1/2 tsp. savory
2 T. chopped green onions   1/8 tsp. pepper
2 T. chopped green pepper   1/4 tsp. salt
2 oz. thin spaghetti, broken into 1/2"-1" pieces   1/3 cup slivered almonds

Cook rice in 1 cup broth, about 35 minutes. Brown spaghetti in margarine 2 minutes. Add 1/2 cup broth, vegetables, & rice. Boil. Cover and reduce heat. Cook until moisture is absorbed, about 10 minutes. Garnish with toasted almonds.

Lemon & Herb Veggies

Serves 4—50 calories & 2 fat grams

1 16-oz. pkg. frozen broccoli, carrots, & cauliflower   2 T. lemon juice
3 T. cooking water   1 clove garlic, minced
1 1/2 tsp. dry basil or 1/4 cup fresh   1 1/2 tsp. margarine
1/4 tsp. cracked black pepper   1/2 tsp. chic. bouillon grains

Cook vegetables in 1/4 cup water, covered until done; drain but reserve liquid. Dissolve bouillon in 3 T. cooking water. Melt margarine in microwave dish, add garlic and cook on high for 30 seconds. Stir in broth, lemon juice, and seasoning. Cook for 2 minutes until thickened. Gently stir into hot vegetables.

Side Dishes

Mini Sweet Potato Casseroles
Serves 4—188 calories & 1 fat gram

4 cup peeled, cubed sweet potato
1/4 cup unsweetened apple juice
1 1/2 T. brown sugar
2 T. buttermilk
2 T. fat-free sour cream
1 tsp. grated orange rind
1 tsp. crushed Gingersnap cookie

1/8 tsp. ground cinnamon
1/8 tsp. ground coriander
1/8 tsp. ground nutmeg
2 egg whites
cooking oil spray
1 tsp. chopped pecans
1/4 tsp. orange extract

Pureé cooked sweet potato in food processor. Mix with apple juice, brown sugar, milk, sour cream, rind, extract, and spices. Let cool. Beat egg whites to stiff peaks, gently fold into potato mixture. Spoon into 4 individual, sprayed mini-casserole dishes. Sprinkle with crushed cookie and chopped pecans. Place casseroles in pan; pour hot water into pan to a depth of 1". Bake at 325° for 30 minutes.

Quick Five Bean Salad
Makes 10 servings—120 calories & 1 fat gram

1 16-oz. can green beans
1 16-oz. can kidney beans
1 16-oz. can garbanzo beans
1 chopped green pepper
1 1/4 cup sugar
dash black pepper

1 16-oz. can wax beans
1 16-oz. can lima beans
1/2 cup chopped onion
1 cup vinegar
2 tsp. oil

Drain all cans of beans. Mix ingredients all together in bowl and chill.

Baked Potato Wedges
Serves 4—122 calories & 0 fat grams

4 washed potatoes
cajun seasoning

cooking oil spray
garlic or seasoning salt

Slice each potato into 8 wedges and spray potatoes with non-fat cooking oil spray. Place on sprayed cookie sheet and sprinkle with seasoning. Bake at 450° for 15-20 minutes or until lightly browned. Serve with fat-free sour cream or salsa.

Desserts

Snow-Frosted Chocolate Brownies

Makes 1 1/2 dozen—97 calories & 4 fat grams per bar

1/2 cup low-calorie margarine
1/4 cup unsweetened cocoa
1 tsp. baking powder
1 1/2 tsp. vanilla extract, divided

1 tsp. chocolate extract
1 cup sugar, divided
3/4 cup flour
3 egg whites, divided

Melt margarine and cocoa. Mix in bowl with flour, baking powder, 3/4 cup sugar, 1 tsp. vanilla extract, and 2 egg whites. Spread in 9" sprayed pan. Beat remaining egg white to stiff peaks. Slowly add remaining sugar & fold in remaining vanilla. Drop spoonfuls of egg whites evenly over mixture and swirl a knife through whites and batter in both directions. Bake at 325° for 25 minutes or until meringue is set and browned. Cool on rack.

Moist Mocha Cake

Serves 9—221 calories and 6 fat grams

1 cup flour
1 cup sugar, divided
1/4 cup + 2 T. unsweetened cocoa, divided
1 1/2 T. instant coffee granules
2 tsp. baking powder
1 cup + 2 T. vanilla ice milk

1/2 cup 1% milk
3 T. vegetable oil
1 tsp. vanilla extract
1 cup boiling water
1/4 tsp. salt
cooking oil spray

Combine flour, 2/3 cup sugar, 1/4 cup cocoa, coffee, baking powder, and salt; mix well. Mix milk, oil, and vanilla and add to dry ingredients; stir well. Spread into sprayed 8" pan. Mix 1/3 cup sugar + 2 T. cocoa. Sprinkle over batter. Pour 1 cup boiling water over batter (do not stir). Bake at 350° for 30 minutes. Serve warm, topped with ice milk.

Peanut Butter Cookies

Makes 4 dozen—48 calories & 2 fat grams per cookie

3/4 cup sugar
1/3 cup peanut butter
1/4 cup margarine, softened
2 egg whites

1 3/4 cup flour
1 tsp. baking soda
1/4 tsp. salt
1/2 tsp. vanilla extract

Combine first 3 ingredients w/ mixer. Add egg whites and vanilla; mix well. Add dry ingredients and mix well. Cover and chill 1 hr. Bake on sprayed sheet at 375° for 10 minutes.

Desserts

Individual Lime Souffles
Serves 6—100 calories & 3 fat grams

3 eggs, separated
1/3 cup sugar
1/4 cup fresh lime juice
2 T. flour
1 1/4 tsp. grated lime rind

2 egg whites
1/8 tsp. salt
1/8 tsp. cream of tartar
2 tsp. powdered sugar

Beat egg yolks with mixer, 5 minutes. Add 2 T. sugar, lime juice, flour, and rind. Set aside.

Beat 5 egg whites until foamy. Add salt, and cr. of tartar, and beat to soft peaks. Slowly add 3 T. + 1 tsp. sugar, beat to stiff peaks. Stir 1/4 egg white mixture into yolk mixture. Fold in remaining egg whites. Spoon into 6 sprayed individual soufflé cups. Bake at 350° for 10 minutes until puffed and golden. Sprinkle w/ powdered sugar. Serve hot.

Pumpkin Cupcakes
Makes 2 dozen—140 calories & 6 fat grams

1 1/2 cups whole wheat flour
1 cup all-purpose flour
3/4 cup sugar
2 T. baking powder
1/2 tsp. ground cinnamon
1/2 tsp. ground nutmeg
1/4 tsp. salt

3 eggs, slightly beaten
1 cup skim milk
1/2 cup oil
1 cup canned pumpkin
3/4 cup chopped raisins
1 T. vanilla

Mix dry ingredients. Mix remaining ingredients and add to dry; mix. Bake at 350° for 20 minutes.

Crunchy-Topped Chocolate Cake
Serves 8—195 calories & 6 fat grams

1/2 cup buttermilk
3 T. oil
1 egg
3/4 cup flour
1/2 cup wheat bran cereal flakes, crushed

3 T. unsweetened cocoa
1/2 tsp. baking soda
1/2 tsp. almond extract
2/3 cup packed brown sugar
2 T. brown sugar

Beat milk, oil, and egg for 1 minute; add extract. Mix flour, 2/3 cup brown sugar, baking soda, and cocoa. Stir into wet mixture; beat 2 minutes. Put in 8" pan, top w/ cereal and 2 T. brown sugar. Microwave on medium for 6 minutes, rotating after 1 minute.

My Favorite Recipes

My Favorite Recipe

Recipe _____

Serves _____ Fat gm. _____ Calories _____

Ingredients

_____   _____
_____   _____
_____   _____
_____   _____
_____   _____
_____   _____
_____   _____

Directions

_____
_____
_____
_____
_____
_____
_____

Comments

_____
_____
_____

A wife who drives from the back seat isn't any worse
than a husband who cooks from the dining room."
—Anonymous

My Favorite Recipe

Recipe _____

Serves _____   Fat gm. _____   Calories _____

Ingredients

_____   _____
_____   _____
_____   _____
_____   _____
_____   _____
_____   _____
_____   _____

Directions

_____
_____
_____
_____
_____
_____
_____
_____

Comments

_____
_____
_____

Keep freshly-cut fruits from browning by tossing them with a little lemon juice.

My Favorite Recipe

Recipe _____

Serves _____   Fat gm. _____   Calories _____

Ingredients

_____   _____
_____   _____
_____   _____
_____   _____
_____   _____
_____   _____
_____   _____

Directions

_____
_____
_____
_____
_____
_____
_____
_____
_____

Comments

_____
_____
_____

*"There's one thing more exasperating than a wife who can
cook and won't—and that's a wife who can't cook and will."*
–Robert Frost

My Favorite Recipe

Recipe _____

Serves _____ Fat gm. _____ Calories _____

Ingredients

_____   _____

_____   _____

_____   _____

_____   _____

_____   _____

_____   _____

_____   _____

Directions

_____

_____

_____

_____

_____

_____

_____

_____

Comments

_____

_____

_____

*"Americans are getting stronger. Twenty years ago, it took two
people to carry $25 worth of groceries. Today, a child can do it."*
—Anonymous

My Favorite Recipe

Recipe _____

Serves _____   Fat gm. _____   Calories _____

Ingredients

_____   _____
_____   _____
_____   _____
_____   _____
_____   _____
_____   _____
_____   _____

Directions

_____
_____
_____
_____
_____
_____
_____

Comments

_____
_____
_____

"Behind every successful man stands a proud
wife and a surprised mother-in-law."
–Anonymous

My Favorite Recipe

Recipe _____

Serves _____ Fat gm. _____ Calories _____

Ingredients

_____   _____

_____   _____

_____   _____

_____   _____

_____   _____

_____   _____

_____   _____

Directions

_____

_____

_____

_____

_____

_____

_____

_____

Comments

_____

_____

_____

Mealtime: When youngsters sit down to continue eating.

My Favorite Recipe

Recipe _____

Serves _____   Fat gm. _____   Calories _____

Ingredients

_____   _____

_____   _____

_____   _____

_____   _____

_____   _____

_____   _____

_____   _____

Directions

_____

_____

_____

_____

_____

_____

_____

_____

Comments

_____

_____

_____

"It isn't so much what's on the table that matters, as who's on the chairs."
—W. S. Gilbert

A Final Word

You made it through 60 days! That's quite an achievement. By now you should be considerably more aware of calories and fat grams when making food selections. You're more conscious of what, and more importantly why, you were over-eating. This is the beginning of a lifetime of better health.

If you have more weight to lose pick up another copy of this book and continue to record your food choices and the emotions that influence them. Many people continue journaling simply to maintain. Don't be discouraged if you're losing weight slowly; what's important is that you're consistently moving in the right direction. You now have the knowledge and determination to become thinner. Your new habits will slowly, but surely, help you realize your ultimate goal.

Once you've achieved your desired weight, keep your journal close-by so you can review it should you find yourself slipping back into unhealthy patterns. Reviewing the emotions that plagued you in the past and seeing how you learned to overcome them will strengthen your resolve to get back on track.

We are very proud to have assisted you on your journey toward improved fitness and health. We're glad to have provided you with useful information, encouragement, and some light-hearted thoughts along the way. Your comments or suggestions will be warmly received. Congratulations on an admirable achievement!

Notes:

Notes:

The Forever Fit Group, Ltd

Order Form

To purchase additional copies of *The 60-Day Food and Fitness Program*, please fill out:

Number of books	_____	x	$14.99	_____
Shipping per book	_____	x	$2.95	_____
			Total	_____

Make checks payable to:

The Forever Fit Group, Ltd.

Mail your order to:

The Forever Fit Group, Ltd.
4145 Parklawn Ave. Suite 338
Edina, MN 55435

Ship to:

Name: _____

Address: _____

City: _____ State: _____ Zip: _____

Phone: _____

Custom printing available. Inquire by phone or in writing.
For large custom orders, or to establish ongoing accounts
for health clubs, diet centers or hospitals, please call.

The Forever Fit Group, Ltd. at (952) 835-9998.